The *Source*®
for
Phonological Awareness

Karin L. Johnson
Barbara A. Roseman

Skill: Phonological Awareness
Ages: 4 through 8
Grades: PreK through Third

LinguiSystems, Inc.
3100 4th Avenue
East Moline, IL 61244-9700
1-800 PRO IDEA
1-800-776-4332

FAX: 1-800-577-4555
E-mail: service@linguisystems.com
Web: www.linguisystems.com
TDD: 1-800-933-8331
(for those with hearing impairments)

Printed in the U.S.A.

ISBN 0-7606-0493-2

Karin L. Johnson

Barbara A. Roseman

Karin L. Johnson, M.A., CCC-SLP, is Professor Emerita from Augustana College in Rock Island, Illinois. She was formally director of the Communication Sciences and Disorders Department.

Barbara A. Roseman, M.A., CCC-SLP, is an associate professor in Communication Sciences and Disorders at Augustana College in Rock Island, Illinois. She is also the director of the Augustana College Center for Communicative Disorders.

Karin and Barbara have co-authored numerous publications in the areas of motor speech disorders, narratives, birth-to-three intervention, metalinguistics, and fluency. Their most recent LinguiSystems publications include *Easy Does It for Fluency—Preschool-Primary*, *Easy Does It for Fluency—Intermediate*, and *Take Home: Fluency*.

Dedication

To our husbands for their loving support and encouragement

Edited by Barb Truman
Illustrations by Margaret Warner
Page layout by Denise L. Kelly
Cover design by Mike Paustian

Table of Contents

Introduction

When Dr. G. Reid Lyon, Chief of the Child Development and Behavior Branch of the National Institute of Child Health and Human Development (NICHD), spoke before the Subcommittee on Educational Reform (2001), it was apparent that the National Institutes of Health were concerned about teaching and learning in today's schools. He spoke specifically of longitudinal studies supported through the NICHD which indicate that "school failure has devastating consequences with respect to self-esteem, social development, and opportunities for advanced education and meaningful employment" (p. 1). "Nowhere" he continued, "are these consequences more apparent than when children fail to learn to read," because "the development of reading skills serves as the major foundational academic ability for all school-based learning" (p. 1).

Unfortunately, a significant number of children experience reading problems. Lyon spoke of a 1998 study reported by the National Center for Educational Statistics which revealed that 38 percent of fourth graders in the United States cannot read and understand a simple short paragraph. Based on this percent, he estimated that at least 20 million school-aged children in the United States "suffer from reading failure" (2001, p. 5).

According to studies supported by the Department of Education as well as the National Science Foundation (NSF), the process of learning to read begins early in a child's life. By the time children receive formal schooling, the process has clearly begun. If basic skills are not achieved by age nine, children face "a lifetime of illiteracy" (Lyon 2001, p. 4).

Factors related to language development, and especially those related to phonological processing abilities, have been found to be particularly critical to the development of reading and spelling. Included in phonological processing is phonological awareness.

What is phonological awareness?

Phonological awareness refers to the ability to recognize that speech is made up of sentences that can be broken down into words, syllables, intrasyllabic units, and phonemes as well as the ability to talk about, reflect upon, and manipulate these components. Phonological awareness occurs when children recognize that there are sounds in words and that these sounds can be talked about, reflected upon, and manipulated.

Does phonological awareness relate to reading and spelling?

Phonological awareness abilities have been associated with the ability to read and spell. Alexander et al. (1991) conceptualized phonological awareness as "a kind of understanding or awareness that allows children to see the connections between written and oral language" (p. 196).

Researchers have indicated that a lack of awareness of the sounds contained in words will be followed by an inability to associate these sounds with symbols (Adams and Bruck 1995, Beck and Juel 1995). In fact, according to Torgeson (1995), children with dyslexia have been consistently more impaired in phonological awareness skills than any other verbal and nonverbal skill tested.

How does phonological awareness relate to reading?

Strong evidence for the causal relationship between phonological awareness and reading comes from studies of instruction in phonological awareness. In general, these studies have found that phonological awareness training increases speech sound awareness and, in turn, reading achievement (Bradley and Bryant 1983; Fox and Routh 1984; Lie 1991; Lundberg, Frost, & Peterson 1988).

Some studies have found phonological awareness skills to have a predictive relation to reading. In fact, a child's level of phonological awareness on entering school is widely believed to be the strongest predictor of the success that a child will have in learning to read (Adams 1990, Stanovich 1986). A reciprocal relationship has also been described. For example, Perfetti (1991) reported that some phonological awareness deficits may result because of poor reading abilities. Children with reading disorders have less experience and skill in using the alphabet and therefore may not acquire the same level of speech sound awareness as normal reading peers.

How does phonological awareness relate to spelling?

The relationship between phonological awareness and spelling development also has been documented (Goswami & Bryant 1990, Lundberg et al. 1988). Clarke-Klein (1994) stated, "Phonological awareness (implicit and explicit) is fundamental to spelling acquisition and develops in gradual and predictable manners" (p. 44).

How does phonological awareness relate to reading and spelling development?

Ellis (1997) described the relationship of reading, spelling, and phonological awareness as a symbiotic development in which "they interact reciprocally over time" (p. 289). Both reading and spelling are part of normal language development. Goswami & Bryant (1990) maintained that reading and spelling interrelate but function independently. Ehri (1997) stated that "learning to read and learning to spell are one and the same, almost" (p. 237). Among the similarities she noted are similar stages of development for reading and spelling. She also maintains that the processes by which we read and spell words are similar; we can read and spell by accessing memory, by decoding, and by analogy.

> Children learn to read and spell in the following ways:
>
> **Memory**—by accessing familiar words represented in memory
>
> **Invention**—by decoding the word by applying knowledge of sound-symbol associations to invent a plausible pronunciation or spelling
>
> **Analogy**—by comparing an unfamiliar word to a familiar one stored in memory
>
> (Ehri 1997)

Differences in spelling and reading also exist. Ehri (1997) noted that "whereas grapheme-phoneme relations are used for reading, phoneme-grapheme relations are used for spelling" (p. 243). Also, reading requires blending skills as one "must assemble a unified pronunciation from the separately decoded parts," whereas "spelling requires segmentation skills to pull apart and distinguish the phonemes to be spelled with graphemes" (Ehri 1997, p. 251). Reading differs from spelling because reading involves one response—pronouncing a word—whereas spelling involves multiple responses—writing more than one letter in sequence.

> **Phoneme**—the smallest linguistic unit of sound which can signal a difference in meaning
>
> **Grapheme**—the smallest unit of writing or printing that distinguishes one meaning from another; a grapheme might consist of more than one letter.

Nonetheless, Ehri (1997) asserted, "The major task in learning to read and spell is to become sufficiently familiar with the spelling of words so that information about their letters is retained in memory and enables them to be read or spelled easily" (p. 242). Basic to both reading and spelling is an understanding of the alphabetic system. Mastery of the alphabetic system includes knowledge about letters, how to relate phonemes to graphemes, and how to segment and blend phonemes of words and then determine the graphemes that correspond to those sound—all skills associated with phonological awareness.

An **alphabetic system** is one in which letters and groups of letters represent meaningful units related to the history of the English language development (Moats 1998) as opposed to a phonetic system in which one letter represents one speech sound.

Why was this book developed?

The importance of phonological awareness to the development of literacy skills, particularly to reading and spelling, is clear. As speech-language pathologists (SLPs), reading disabilities teachers, learning disabilities teachers, and classroom teachers, we need to fully understand phonological awareness and its role in normal development as well as its relationship to disorders of reading and spelling. Likewise, we need to know how to organize phonological awareness activities in order to promote normal development as well as to prevent or remediate problems with phonological awareness.

The Source for Phonological Awareness was designed for those professionals who work with children from preschool through third grade to aid in prevention as well as habilitation of reading problems. It is organized to answer the following questions:

Chapter 1: What is phonological awareness?

Chapter 2: What is the relationship between reading and spelling development and the development of phonological awareness?

Chapter 3: What factors are associated with reading and spelling disabilities?

Chapter 4: How is phonological awareness assessed?

Chapter 5: How are phonological awareness skills developed?

Finally, concluding information is shared and Appendices are provided to supplement information about assessment (Chapter 4) and intervention (Chapter 5).

Karin and Barbara

Note: *The Source for Phonological Awareness* uses phonetic symbols to indicate sounds; these symbols are placed within slashes. When clarification is needed, parentheses are used [e.g., /ʃ/ (sh)].

Chapter 1

What is phonological awareness?

There is considerable evidence in support of a language basis for many reading and spelling disabilities. Of particular concern for this book are those aspects of language associated with phonology and especially those associated with phonological awareness.

> **Phonology** refers to the sound system of language.

Before focusing on phonological awareness, it is helpful to consider phonological processing as a whole.

What is phonological processing?

Phonological processing refers to "an individual's mental operations that make use of the phonological or sound structure of oral language when he or she is learning how to decode written language" (Torgeson, Wagner, & Rashotte 1994, p. 276). According to Catts and Kamhi (1999a), phonological processing includes four areas: awareness, production, retrieval, and memory.

◆ **Phonological awareness** refers to the ability to think about, talk about, and manipulate speech sounds in words.

◆ **Phonological production** refers to the ability to use the rules of the sound system to produce words.

◆ **Phonological retrieval** refers to the ability to access words from long-term memory.

◆ **Phonological memory** refers to the "encoding and storage of phonological information in memory" (Catts & Kamhi 1999a, p. 113). According to Wagner, Torgesen, and Rashotte (1999), phonological information is coded temporarily in short-term memory.

Deficits in any of these areas or any combinations of these areas may result in problems with reading and spelling. Phonological awareness is the area, however, most consistently associated with reading and spelling disabilities.

What does phonological awareness include?

Phonological awareness occurs when children recognize that sentences are made of words that can be broken down into syllables, intrasyllabic units, and phonemes and that these units can be talked about, reflected upon, and manipulated. It includes an awareness of components such as words, sounds, syllables, onsets, rimes, and beginning/middle/ending sounds that can be segmented, blended, and manipulated.

> The **rime** is determined by the vowel. The **onset** is anything to the left of the vowel; the **rime** is the vowel plus whatever follows it in the syllable. For example, in *pigs*, *p* = onset and *-igs* = rime or in *sprint*, *spr* = onset and *-int* = rime. A rime may also stand alone (e.g., *I* = rime or *in* = rime).

To understand phonological awareness, it is important to distinguish it from similar terminology.

How is phonological awareness different from speech discrimination?

Phonological awareness differs from speech discrimination because the "ability to detect or discriminate even slight differences between two spoken words does not necessarily indicate an awareness of the nature of the difference" (Snow, Burns, & Griffin 1998, p. 52). A child may be able to tell whether two sounds are the same or different (speech discrimination) but be unable to apply this information at the meaning level (phonological awareness). For example, a child may be able to tell that /b/ and /k/ are different and that *bat* and *cat* are different without being able to understand that differences in meaning are coded by the change in the initial phonemes.

Children who possess speech discrimination problems will most likely also have problems with phonological awareness; however, children with good speech discrimination may still have problems with phonological awareness. While good phonological abilities have been related to reading success, good speech discrimination has not (Snow et al. 1998).

How is phonological awareness different from phonics?

Phonological awareness must also be distinguished from phonics, "the system by which symbols represent sounds in the alphabetic writing system" (Adams et al. 1998, p. 3). Moats (1998) asserted that "one of the most fundamental flaws found in almost all phonics programs, including traditional ones, is that they teach the code backwards. That is, phonics programs go from letter to sound instead of from sound to letter" (p. 44). She stated that, from a historical perspective, speech was not learned from reading, but rather print language was invented to represent speech; therefore, it is more logical to teach awareness of the sound system first and then "anchor" letters to it. Furthermore, phonics "presumes a working awareness of the phonemic composition of words" that may not be present if children have phonological awareness deficits (Snow et al. 1998, p. 55). Without phonological/phonemic awareness, children will not be able to benefit from work on phonics.

How is phonological awareness different from phonemic awareness?

Finally, **phonological awareness** must be distinguished from **phonemic awareness**. While some authors use the terms interchangeably, others see phonological awareness as a broad term encompassing phonemic awareness. Snow et al. (1998) defined phonological awareness as "the general ability to attend to the sounds of language as distinct from its meaning" (p. 52), whereas phonemic awareness refers to "the insight that every spoken word can be conceived as a sequence of phonemes" (p. 52). Swank (1994) described two levels of phonological awareness. One level involves awareness of syllabic and intrasyllabic segments related to onsets and rimes. This level requires little metacognitive ability and develops before a child learns the alphabetic principle.

> **Metacognition** refers to the ability to talk about and reflect upon one's thinking process.

The second level, on the other hand, develops later with the acquisition of the alphabetic principle and requires greater metacognitive abilities. It involves phonemic awareness (Swank 1994), "the highest level in the hierarchy of phonological awareness skills" (Lombardino et al. 1997, p. 334).

> The **alphabetic principle** is the principle that explains how sounds of speech (phonemes) become associated with the letters of the alphabet (phonics)" (Lyon 2001, p.1).

Throughout this book we will use the broad meaning of **phonological awareness**, referring to the general ability to recognize and manipulate the sounds of language and encompassing both phonological and phonemic awareness abilities as seen in child development from preschool through first grade.

Chapter 2

What is the relationship between reading and spelling development and the development of phonological awareness?

The relationship between the development of phonological awareness and the development of reading and spelling is critical. Because the focus of this book is on the relationship between phonological awareness and literacy, it is important to understand language development as it relates to development of reading, spelling, and particularly phonological awareness.

This chapter begins with a definition of language and a review of how spoken language and print language are both similar and different. Then it provides a brief overview of normal language development that focuses on phonological development. An overview of normal reading and spelling development follows. This chapter ends with an overview of the development of phonological awareness skills.

What is language?

In 1982 the American Speech-Language-Hearing Association (ASHA) adopted the following definition of language:

"Language is a complex and dynamic system of conventional symbols that is used in various modes for thought and communication . . . [and] as a rule-governed behavior, is described by at least five parameters—phonologic, morphologic, syntactic, semantic, and pragmatic" (ASHA 1995, pp. III-155).

Typically, these parameters are grouped in three categories: form (phonology, morphology, and syntax), content (semantics), and use (pragmatics).

With regard to spoken language, **phonology** refers to the sound system of language. Phonology includes the sound and syllable structure of language and the rules for prohibition and occurrence of these forms. It also encompasses the suprasegmental aspects of language, including stress, intonation, and pausing.

Morphology deals with the rules for word forms (e.g., grammatical structures). Morphophonology represents an overlap of phonology and morphology. Some words change in phonologic form to convey changes in meaning (e.g., read /rid/ as present tense and read /rɛd/ as past tense).

Similar to morphology is **syntax**, which refers to word order in phrases and sentences.

The **semantic** parameter of language deals with the ways language conveys meaning. It includes a person's lexicon, "stored information about the meanings and pronunciations of words" as well as word relationships (Snow, Burns, & Griffin 1998, p. 47).

Finally, **pragmatics** refers to the use of language. It encompasses the use of contexts— intentional, speaker, situation, and linguistic—to guide the selection of the semantic, syntactic, morphologic, and phonologic features of the communication act.

Two other critical aspects of language need to be considered: **world knowledge** and **nonverbal language**. World knowledge refers to "autobiographical and experiential understanding and memory of events reflecting personal and cultural interpretations" (Owens 1996, p. 465). World knowledge includes an understanding of conversational, narrative, and expository discourse, also known as *text knowledge*. Nonverbal language as conveyed through facial expressions and gestures is used to supplement, reinforce, clarify, or contradict spoken language.

A **text** is any passage, spoken or written, that stands together as a unified whole. It may be as short as a sentence or as long as a lecture or a book. Three types of **discourse** (i.e., continuous communication of ideas) are typically included in text knowledge:

- **conversation**
  (interacting in which partners have roughly equal parts)

- **narratives** (telling stories)

- **expository texts** (sharing of factual or technical information)

(Nelson 1998)

How does oral language relate to print language?

Language is not limited to the oral modality; it also encompasses the visual modality. Berninger (2000) asserted that children learn four language systems: an aural system (receptive language through the ear); an oral system (spoken language through the mouth); a printed system (receptive language through the eye); and a written system (expressive language through the hand).

Aural System (Language by ear)	Oral System (Language by mouth)	Print System (Language by eye)	Written System (Language by hand)
Receptive	Expressive	Receptive	Expressive
Heard words	Spoken words	Printed words	Written words

The visual/print aspects of language include reading, writing, and spelling. Even though both oral and print language require competence in understanding and using all of the parameters described previously, differences in all areas also occur.

Reading and Writing

In print, the **phonologic/morphophonologic** parameter (i.e., the sounds and syllables) must be converted to print form through the use of graphemes and punctuation, but this process is not a simple phoneme to grapheme conversion. Readers and writers must also master rules of spelling. Suprasegmental aspects must be conveyed in print through descriptions or punctuation or both. **Syntactic** and **morphologic** forms are used to create printed words and sentences, but in print, syntactic forms tend to be more complex and more formal. In print as in spoken language, **semantic** information is conveyed by printed words and linguistic relations, but in print, semantic forms generally are more decontextualized than in spoken language (i.e., readers do not have the context clues to help them understand the words). **Pragmatically**, a writer must consider the reader's perspective and background and select semantic, syntactic, and morphologic forms appropriate to the reader as well as to the linguistic, situation, and intentional contexts. Since readers cannot ask for clarification, writers must anticipate confusions and attempt to eliminate ambiguities more diligently than speakers in an interactive situation.

Readers and writers must rely on their **world knowledge** and **text knowledge** to guide their organizational structure. In addition, print conventions related to text types (e.g., variations for poetry, scripts, narratives, and expository texts), print features (e.g., graphs, tables, and illustrations), and print formats (e.g., bold print and italics) all convey information in printed texts. "Unlike spoken language, written language is removed from the present, thus requiring a greater focus on the linguistic information being written or read because of minimal, if any, nonlinguistic cues" (Apel 2002, p. 6). **Nonverbal** aspects of communication must be described in print language or illustrated through pictures or drawings. Finally, "reading, writing, and spelling require a level of active awareness and thought about language that spoken language generally does not" (Apel 2002, p. 6). They require **metalinguistic** skills related to phonological awareness.

> **Metalinguistics** refers to the ability to think about, talk about, and manipulate language.

A reciprocal relationship exists between oral and print language. Strong oral language skills are needed to develop strong reading skills, but strong reading abilities are needed to continue to develop oral language. Additionally, the relationship between phonological awareness and reading appears to be reciprocal "in that each facilitates and is facilitated by the other" (Chafouleas et al. 1997, p. 334). Simple phonological awareness skills seem to be precursors to reading, whereas more complex phonological awareness skills seem to result from reading (Chafouleas et al. 1997).

There seem to be two facets of phonological awareness, an implicit awareness of syllables and rhyme early in development and a later explicit ability to segment at the phoneme level. Early reading development seems to utilize the implicit aspect of phonological awareness, whereas reading ability promotes the later developing explicit aspects of phonological awareness (Ellis 1997, p. 288).

Snow, Scarborough, and Burns (1999) summarized research findings regarding skilled readers in the following way:

◆ "Highly skilled readers fixate their eyes very briefly (for about 1/4 of a second) on virtually every word on the printed page, even though they are entirely unaware of doing so" (p. 50).

◆ "The printed words are very rapidly represented by the brain both orthographically (i.e., as letter sequences) and phonologically (i.e., as the series of speech segments that the letters are most likely to represent). The process of creating phonological representation of printed words, called *decoding*, is possible because extensive knowledge about the correspondences between spellings and pronunciations of words has been built up from years of instruction and practice" (p. 50-51).

◆ "Using both orthographic and phonological representations, the mental dictionary is quickly searched for an entry that most closely matches the input with respect to its pronunciation and/or spelling. When a satisfactory match is found, we say that the printed word has been "recognized." At this point, we can now retrieve all the other information that has been stored about the word, including its meanings and syntactic constraints" (p. 51).

◆ "Skilled readers rarely try to recognize words by guessing their identities on the basis of the context because decoding is a far more accurate and efficient approach. Research has shown that there is only a slim chance of guessing a word correctly from contextual clues alone" (p. 51).

◆ "As successive words from a text are recognized, skilled readers apply their general language skills (syntactic, morphological, semantic, and pragmatic) and background knowledge to derive a cohesive understanding of the sentence being read and of the larger text in which it is embedded. In other words, once printed words have been recognized, the process of reading comprehension is nearly identical to the process of listening comprehension" (p. 51).

◆ "Good readers constantly monitor their comprehension to make sure that the result makes good sense. Comprehension will suffer if a word has been incorrectly recognized, if the text includes words that are not in the reader's oral vocabulary, if the linguistic structure of the sentence is overly complex, or if the topic of the reading material is so unfamiliar that the reader cannot make inferences (i.e., "read between the lines") that are necessary to understanding of the text" (p. 51).

◆ "All of these cognitive operations are carried out quickly and relatively effortlessly, such that skilled reading is automated and fluent" (p. 51).

Spelling

Like reading, spelling is related to oral communication. Spelling is not simply the means by which phonemes are converted to graphemes. According to Templeton (2002), ". . . the English spelling system has developed in such a way that words that are related in meaning are often related in spelling as well . . ." (p. 4). Spelling, therefore, interacts in a critical way with the phonologic/graphophonologic, syntactic/ morphologic, and semantic parameters of language. Morris and Perney (1984) reported that the encoding process (sound to letter) involved in spelling is "the reciprocal of the decoding task facing the beginning reader (letter to sound)" (p. 455) and the practice of manipulating and sequencing sound-letter relationships in the process of creating invented spellings has been shown to have "a carryover effect to learning to read" (p. 455).

> After children develop an awareness of alphabet letter names, they develop a realization that letters represent speech sounds, but their knowledge of standard orthography is incomplete. As a result, when they attempt to spell words, they **invent** spellings based on their knowledge of letter names coupled with some sound-letter correspondences and driven by attention to articulatory phonetic features.

How does oral language develop in young children?

Overview

While a child's first year is filled with many important developmental milestones that are prerequisites for acquiring speech and language, typically, children begin to talk at around 12 months. By 18 months, they are combining words into simple two-word combinations and by 24 months, are beginning to use short, simple sentences. During the remainder of the preschool years, children acquire most of the basics of syntactic and semantic development. They also learn to use language to inform, control, ritualize, express feelings, and imagine.

Informing refers to giving and getting information.

Controlling refers to influencing or controlling the listener's behaviors.

Ritualizing refers to language related to specific social or cultural situations.

Expressing feelings refers to expressing or responding to attitudes and feelings.

Imagining refers to talking in creative or imaginary situations.

Preschool children also begin to develop an understanding of narratives, and they begin to tell narratives, including accounts, recounts, eventcasts, and simple stories within the framework of their cultural experiences. Additionally, they increase their phonological skills as they gradually master the sounds of their language. Hodson (1994) summarized findings on normal development in this way: ". . . phonologically normal children communicate with words by two years, have 'adult-like' speech by age four, and 'adult-standard' speech by age seven" (p. 6).

Narrative Types

Account—a narrative in which the speaker relates a past experience that the listener did not share

Recount—a narrative in which the speaker relates a past experience in which both the speaker and listener participated

Eventcast—a narrative that describes a current or anticipated event

Story—a familiar or created story

(Owens 1996)

Phonological Production

A more in-depth look at the development of phonological skills reveals that most children produce stops (/b, p, t, d, g, k/), nasals (/m, n/), and glides (/w, j (y)/) in consonant (C) and vowel (V) combinations by 18 months. The typical two-year-old produces eight to nine initial consonants, five to six final consonants, and at least one consonant cluster; additionally, two-year-olds produce the following syllable structures involving consonants and vowels: CV, VC, CVC, and CVCV, although some final consonant deletions may occur with CVC words (Stoel-Gammon 1987). At around two years of age, children develop a rule-based approach to production of words that involves simplifying adult forms. These simplifications are described as *phonological processes*.

It is important not to confuse **phonological processes**, the rules young children use to simplify adult pronunciations, with **phonological processing**, a person's mental operations that make use of the phonological system when he or she is learning to read and write. (See Chapter 1 for discussion of phonological processing, page 9.)

Three types of simplification processes occur:

◆ syllable simplification

◆ sound substitutions

◆ sound assimilations (i.e., making one sound like or similar to another sound in the word, like *toat/coat*)

These phonological processes drop out when the child becomes capable of producing adult forms (Stoel-Gammon & Dunn 1985). Examples of these simplification processes are listed below:

Processes Disappearing by Three Years	Processes Persisting at Three Years
Unstressed Syllable Deletion: omission of the unstressed syllable or syllables (*nana* for *banana*)	Cluster Reduction: omission of one sound in a two- or three-consonant sequence (*poon* for *spoon*)
Final Consonant Deletion: omission of the final consonant or consonant cluster (*ca* for *cat*)	Epenthesis: addition of "uh" between two consonants in a consonant cluster or after a voiced stop (*buhlue* for *blue* or *biguh* for *big*)
Doubling: repetition of a monosyllabic word two times (*pipi* for *pig* or *gogo* for *go*)	Gliding: substitution of /w/or /j/ (y) for /r/ or /l/ (*wight* for *light*)
Diminutization: addition of /i/ at the end of a word (*cupi* for *cup*)	Vocalization: substitution of a vowel for /r/ or /l/ (*cao* for *car*)
Velar Fronting: substitution of a sound made more toward the front of the mouth for a sound made at the back of the mouth (*tan* for *can*)	Stopping: substitution of a sound that stops for one that continues (*tun* for *sun*)
Consonant Assimilation: substitution of a sound that is more similar to another sound in the word (*momey* for *money*)	Depalatalization: substitution of a sound made in an area other than the palate (*sip* for *ship*)
Reduplication: repetition of a syllable in a two-syllable word, usually the first syllable (*baba* for *bottle*)	Final devoicing: omission of voicing on the final sound of a word (*back* for *bag*)
Prevocalic Voicing: substitution of a voiced for a voiceless sound in the beginning of a word (*gan* for *can*)	

By age three, most children are generally intelligible. By four years, phonological simplification processes (e.g., stopping and fronting) and sound omissions are rare. By six years, improvements in producing multisyllabic words are noted. "By age seven, children should be able to produce common multisyllabic words and, in general, have phonologies comparable to adults in their linguistic community" (Hodson 1994, p. 6).

Metalinguistics

Preschool children also begin to develop some metalinguistic skills. In other words, they begin to think about, talk about, and manipulate language. Tunmer, Herriman, and Nesdale (1988) identified four types of metalinguistic abilities that may play a role in the development of reading and spelling.

◆ *Phonological Awareness*

Phonological awareness is the ability to think about, talk about, and manipulate the sounds of language.

◆ *Word Awareness*

Word awareness is the ability to talk about and think about words, their meanings, and their boundaries. The ability to talk about and think about phonemes "presupposes the ability to reflect on words, although not vice versa" (Tunmer et al. 1988, p. 137). For this reason, word awareness is usually included within the general term "*phonological awareness*."

◆ *Syntactic Awareness*

Syntactic awareness is the ability to use one's knowledge of intrasentential (within sentence) groupings of words (i.e., word order) to comprehend texts. Syntactic awareness enables readers to use their knowledge of the syntactic relations within sentences to identify unfamiliar words. Additionally, it may help beginning readers to deal with spelling patterns that are associated with more than one pronunciation (e.g., *cough-dough*) or unusual pronunciations (e.g., *yacht*) by using syntactic context to help them choose the right word (Tunmer et al. 1988).

◆ *Pragmatic Awareness*

Pragmatic awareness involves using knowledge of pragmatic rules and inferencing to comprehend texts at the intersentential (between sentences) level (Tunmer et al. 1988).

◆ *Metatextual Awareness*

We would add to the four metalinguistic awarenesses suggested by Tunmer et al. (1988) a fifth metalinguistic skill—metatextual awareness— the ability to talk about, think about, and manipulate the structure of a text (narrative or expository). Knowledge of how a text is organized can be helpful in text comprehension.

What is the impact of metalinguistics on reading and spelling?

Phonological and word awareness skills appear to be more important during early stages of reading and spelling when the emphasis is on decoding, whereas pragmatic and textual knowledge appear to be more important in later stages when the emphasis is on comprehension. Even so, pragmatic awareness and text awareness skills begin to develop during the preschool years. Children develop metanarrative skills as they learn to talk about stories: characters, time, place, and action. They develop metapragmatic skills as they learn to role-play different people and characters (e.g., pretending to talk like the mommy or doctor during playtime). Syntactic awareness appears to be important for both comprehension and decoding.

How does reading develop?

Frith (1985) described three stages of reading development:

- ◆ logographic

- ◆ alphabetic

- ◆ orthographic

Moats (1998) described four stages, dividing Frith's alphabetic stage into two stages: early alphabetic and mature alphabetic.

◆ *Logographic Stage*

The logographic stage is a pre-alphabetic stage or precommunicative stage in which children recognize associations between unanalyzed words and printed word forms without knowledge of sound-symbol associations. For example, at this stage, they recognize words printed on common objects (e.g., *Cheerios* on the cereal box). Children do so based on the word's visual features. They do not yet realize that words are composed of phonemes represented by letters (Moats 1998).

◆ *Alphabetic Stage*

Early or novice alphabetic
During this stage, children use partial phonetic cues to recognize words. They focus on beginning and ending letters in words. They develop some sound-symbol associations to use in reading words that were not present in the logographic stage, but they have not yet acquired full alphabetic knowledge to use in decoding words (Moats 1998).

Mature alphabetic

At this stage, children learn to use sound-symbol (phoneme-grapheme) associations to decode unfamiliar words (Moats 1998).

> A **phoneme** is the smallest meaningful sound unit in a language whereas a **grapheme** is a functional print unit that represents a phoneme. For example, the phoneme /k/ may be represented by the graphemes K, CK, C, or CH. There are approximately 40 phonemes in English and 70 graphemes (letters/letter combinations) to symbolize them (Ehri 2000).

Children learn basic sound spellings and can use them to decode simple words. They also begin to recognize word patterns (e.g., *-ack, -ell*) and word endings (e.g., *-ed, -ing*) (Moats 1998). "They learn to associate onsets and rimes with strings of letters . . . [they] make inferences or analogies about new words on the basis of spelling patterns in words they already know, and . . . they do this as soon as they begin to read" (Goswami & Bryant 1990, p. 147).

> **Rime stems** (which are sometimes called *phonograms*) form common word patterns (e.g., *-ack, -ell, -ame*). Thirty-seven (37) rime stems can generate 500 primary grade words. (Wylie & Durrell 1970)

◆ *Orthographic Stage*

The last stage is the orthographic stage (Frith 1985, Moats 1998).

> **Orthography** is the study of the writing system of language—how the sounds of language are represented in letters and spelling. It includes knowledge of the rules for positional constraints (i.e., rules for prohibition and occurrence of letters in a language).

At this stage, children learn to use letter sequences and spelling patterns to recognize words without having to go through a phonologic conversion. Children acquire and can store enough knowledge about word patterns (similar letter sequences) that they can recognize words visually. They make greater use of analogy (comparing an unfamiliar word to a familiar word stored in memory) to help them read unfamiliar words. Knowledge of prefixes and suffixes as well as word derivations continues to develop. With these types of information, greater automaticity and fluency in reading gradually develop.

How does spelling develop?

Gentry (1982) and Moats (1995) described stages for spelling development based in part on earlier information reported by Read (1971). Read maintained that children have an unconscious knowledge of English phonology that they apply when learning to spell. He proposed that in their early spelling efforts, children apply phonetic information (information about the articulatory features of sounds) to their sound-symbol efforts.

> **Phonetics** refers to the articulatory or physical characteristics of sounds. In contrast, **phonology** refers to the sound system of a language including the rules for occurrence and prohibition of sounds as well as how they function to convey meaning. As children learn to spell, they use phonetic (articulatory) information about the place and manner of speech sound production to help them associate sounds with graphemes.

Stages of Spelling Development

◆ Precommunicative

◆ Semiphonetic

◆ Phonetic

◆ Transitional

◆ Correct

Precommunicative

Gentry (1982) and Moats (1995) both labeled the first stage of spelling development as *precommunicative*. Children who are exposed to print at home will begin to "write," but since they do not yet know phoneme-grapheme associations, their attempts consist of random sequences of letters and letter-like or number-like forms. Since the children do not yet know word boundaries, their letters run together and the children may write from top to bottom or right to left. Uppercase and lowercase letters are mixed. When shown their writings later, the children cannot read them because there are no phoneme-grapheme relationships.

> A **letter** is a visual unit in print (i.e., any letter in the alphabet—*A, B, C . . . Z*), whereas a **grapheme** is a functional unit of print symbolizing a phoneme (e.g., The phoneme /ʃ/ [sh] may be represented by these graphemes: *SH, S* [sugar], or *TI* [education]).

Semiphonetic

At the semiphonetic stage, children begin to recognize the alphabetic principle. They begin to realize that letters represent speech sounds, but this knowledge is partial. Attempts at writing reveal this awareness with some relationships (e.g., beginning consonants) being present. Letters are strung together in a logical but abbreviated form with one or two letters representing whole words (Moats 1995). Consonants occur more frequently than vowels (e.g., *PL* for *pickle*). Children use a letter name strategy to represent words, sounds, or syllables with letters that match their letter names (e.g., *R* for *are*). Children have to create a system for dealing with consonants that do not have a simple sound-symbol-letter name association. For example, *CH* /tʃ/ is often written as *H* since this is the only letter name that is pronounced with this sound (e.g., "ach"). Similarly, *Y* is often used to spell /w/ since its name is pronounced with this sound (e.g., "wie"). Using this strategy, children at this stage will spell *wife* as *YF*.

Phonetic

The next stage is the phonetic stage (Gentry 1982, Moats 1995). Children gain greater consistency in spelling words using strategies based on their knowledge of letter names and some sound-letter correspondences. "At the phonetic spelling stage, children have at their command a repertoire of letter names and some learned sound-letter associations by which they represent all speech sounds in words systematically" (Moats 1995, p. 37). They segment words into their component sounds and represent each sound with a letter (e.g., *NIS* for *nice*).

Children rely on surface phonetic features, not phonemic or morphemic information, and they rely ". . . heavily on sound segmentation and articulatory-phonetic feedback, so much so that one could term this stage 'spelling by mouth' rather than 'spelling by sound'" (Moats 1995, p. 37). For example, children at this stage spell long vowels by using their letter names (e.g., *DA* for *day*).

Spelling of short vowels is harder. To spell short vowels, children at this stage use what is called the *Vowel Shift*; they "raise their place of articulation from that of the short vowel to the next highest position" (Read 1971, p. 7). They substitute the long vowel nearest to the short vowel in place of articulation and then use the long vowel letter name in the spelling. As a result, spellings like these occur: *fish* /fɪʃ/ → *FES* (E = /i/) and *fell* /fɛl/ → *FALL* (A = /e/). (To see how this works, consider the vowel chart on the next page. This chart shows the location of vowels based on tongue placement—high to low and front to back. The short I /ɪ/ moves up to the long E /i/ and the short E /ɛ/ moves up to the long A /e/.) Back rounded vowels are often spelled with O + W to indicate the articulatory rounding of the lips (e.g., *GOWT* for *goat*).

Vowel and Grapheme Chart

Front Vowels	**High Vowels**	**Back Vowels**

heat   /i/   e

    hit   /ɪ/   i   oo   /u/   hoot

        hay   /e/   a   oo   /ʊ/   hoof

          head   /ɛ/   e   o   /o/   hoe

           hat   /æ/   a   aw   /aʊ/   haw

            high   /aɪ/   a   u   /ʌ/   hut

                                o
                             /a/
                            hot

Low Vowels

Digraphs	**Diphthongs**
oy	/ɔɪ/
ow	/oʊ/

Vowel controlled r's

     /ɛr /   /ar /   /ɔr/

     her   car   horn
     fir
     fur

The effect of the phonetic-feature analysis is also apparent in the spelling of some consonants. For example, when *T* and *D* occur in /r/ clusters (e.g., in *tr-* and *dr-* words such as *truck* and *dragon*), they are often spelled as *CH* or *J* because in English, the /t/ and /d/ become affricated before /r/.

As a result, *truck* is often written as *CHRK* or *CHRUK* and *dragon* is written as *JRAGN* or *JRAGIN*. Children at this stage are also likely to omit nasals in nasal clusters (e.g., *PLAT* for *plan*") because they perceive the nasality to be a feature of the vowel rather than a separate sound.

> An **affricate** is a phoneme that combines a stop and a fricative into one sound. In English, only /tʃ/ (ch) and /dʒ/ (j) are affricates. When /t/ and /d/ precede /r/ in initial /r/ clusters, they take on this affricate quality.

At this stage, children choose letters on the basis of their sounds without regard for conventional rules of English spelling. Nevertheless, their choices are "systematic and perceptually correct" (Gentry 1982, p. 195). If asked to read what they wrote, children at this stage have no trouble doing so.

Transitional

The fourth stage is the transitional stage (Gentry 1982, Moats 1995). Children learn that there are rules for phoneme-grapheme correspondences. Children no longer have to rely on a letter-name strategy. Vowels are included in every syllable. Children begin to use silent letters and to use two letters to spell some vowels. They begin to use vowels before "syllabic *r* even though it is not heard or felt as a separate sound (e.g., *MONSTUR* instead of the phonetic *MOSTR* [monster]" (Gentry 1982, p. 196). They also begin to internalize patterns for spelling some words (e.g., *EIGHTEE* instead of the phonetic *ATE* [eighty])" (Gentry 1982, p. 196). Additionally, some inflectional endings like plural *s* and *-ing* are used (Moats 1995).

Correct

The last stage is the correct (Gentry 1982) or morphophonemic stage (Moats 1995). "After learning the graphemes that represent consonant and vowel spellings within a syllable, children must then learn to recognize common ways in which meaning influences spelling in combination with sound-symbol correspondence" (Moats 1995, p. 40). They learn to spell words with inflectional and derivational morphemes as well as homophones and compound words.

In English there are eight **inflectional morphemes**. They do not change the part of speech of the root word (e.g., plural *s* is an inflectional ending that is added to nouns to indicate more than one, but the category of the word remains a noun). They always occur at the end of the word. The eight inflectional morphemes are: plural *s*, possessive *'s*, past tense *-ed*, comparative *-er*, superlative *-est*, present tense *s*, past participle *-en*, and present participle *-ing*.

Derivational morphemes are prefixes and all non-inflectional suffixes. Typically, they change the part of speech of the word (e.g., *-er* can be a derivational morpheme when added to the word *teach* to create *teacher*. The verb *teach* changes to become a noun *teacher*). Only one inflectional morpheme can be attached to a word (e.g., one cannot say "happierest"), but more than one derivational morpheme (e.g., "enthuse" can become "enthusiastically") or one inflectional and one derivational morpheme (e.g., "friendlier") can be attached to a word.

Inflected endings, such as *-ed*, *-s*, *-ing*, *-er*, and *-est*, are used frequently in children's oral language, but their pronunciations vary depending on the word to which they are attached (e.g., in *rubbed* /rʌbd/ the *-ed* is pronounced as /d/, but in *washed* /waʃt/ the *-ed* is pronounced as /t/, and in *wanted* /wantəd/ it is pronounced as a syllable /əd/). At this stage, children learn to recognize that words have two parts—the word and its ending—both of which they must consider when spelling the word. Correct orthographic spelling continues to develop over the next few years.

What is the relationship between reading and spelling development?

Ehri (1997) argued that "learning to read and learning to spell are one and the same, almost" (p. 237). Reading and spelling differ since reading uses grapheme-phoneme relations whereas spelling uses phoneme-grapheme relations. Also, "the act of reading words from memory involves one response, that of retrieving and pronouncing the words. In contrast, the act of recalling the spellings of words involves multiple responses, that of writing several letters in the correct sequence" (Ehri 2000, p. 33). Lombardino et al. (1997) summarized findings regarding reading and spelling development by noting that "in the early stages of literacy, invented spelling requires some knowledge of the alphabetic principle of English orthography (i.e., mapping of graphemes onto phonemes), whereas the earliest stage of reading does not require the alphabetic mapping of sounds onto letters. However, as soon as children begin to apply the alphabetic principle to the decoding of print, these two skills become highly related" (p. 335).

On the other hand, Ehri (1997) argued that reading and spelling are the same because children learn to read and spell in at least three ways: by memory, by invention, and by analogy. (See the box on page 7 in the introduction.) Children read and spell familiar words by accessing the words in their memory, whereas they read and spell unfamiliar words by invention or by analogy. Additionally, both reading and spelling require knowledge of the alphabetic system. To read and spell, children need to develop phonological awareness skills—blending for reading and segmenting for spelling. Finally, the development of reading and spelling are similar. Ehri described four developmental stages for reading and spelling that parallel those previously described and that reveal a growing knowledge of the alphabetic principle:

◆ *Logographic/Prealphabetic/Precommunicative*

At this stage children read familiar labels and signs based on their salient visual features, and they spell by producing scribbles.

◆ *Partial Alphabetic*

At this stage, children "use their knowledge of letter names or sounds to form connections between salient letters seen in words and sounds detected in pronunciations" (Ehri 2000, p. 28). They either remember words or guess based on context. They cannot decode unfamiliar words. To spell, children "detect and spell partial sounds in words, mainly the more salient consonants and vowels whose names are heard in the words" (Ehri 2000, p. 28).

◆ *Full Alphabetic*

Children can decode unfamiliar words because they know grapheme-phoneme relations. They can invent spellings that are more complete.

◆ *Consolidated Alphabetic*

Children learn the structure of larger units of letter sequences and so they can decode and invent spellings of longer words (e.g., they not only know the grapheme-phoneme components of sequences such as -*est*, but they also know them as a unit). "These units may involve spellings of syllables, or parts of syllables, or affixes appearing at the beginnings or endings of words. Such recurring blends of graphophonemic units become consolidated into larger units" (Ehri 2000, p. 29).

The following chart provides a comparison of the stages of reading and spelling development reviewed on the previous page.

Stages of Reading and Spelling Development

Reading	Reading	Reading & Spelling	Spelling	Spelling
Frith (1985)	**Moats (1998)**	**Ehri (2000)**	**Moats (1995)**	**Gentry (1982)**
Logographic	Logographic	Logographic/ Pre-alphabetic/ Precommunicative	Precommunicative	Precommunicative
Alphabetic	Novice/ early alphabetic	Partial alphabetic	Semiphonetic	Semiphonetic
	Mature alphabetic	Full alphabetic	Phonetic	Phonetic
Orthographic	Orthographic	Consolidated	Transitional	Transitional
			Morpho-phonemic	Correct

How does phonological awareness develop?

As indicated at the outset, development of phonological awareness has been shown to be related to reading and spelling development. While phonological awareness is not the only factor involved in reading and spelling, there is a large body of research that supports a consistent relationship between phonological awareness and early reading and spelling development (Lombardino et al. 1997). It is important, then, to know how phonological awareness skills develop.

Hodson (2002) described the following developmental sequence for metaphonological (phonological awareness) skills. Pre-kindergarten children (four-year-olds) should be able to engage in rhyming and alliteration tasks. While the role of rhyming is somewhat controversial, there is general agreement that it makes ". . . an independent contribution to literacy skills" (Hodson 1994, p. 7). Goswami and Bryant (1992) stated that ". . . analogy is the essential link in the chain that starts with a child's preschool experiences with rhyme and ends with skilled reading and writing" (p. 62). When young children hear and produce rhymes, they gradually begin to recognize that some words have common rimes. The children form categories of words, which they will recognize when they begin to read and spell. They can use this information to make inferences (i.e., to make analogies) about new words.

Preschoolers should also be able to segment words into syllables and to blend and manipulate (e.g., delete, substitute, or reverse) syllables, with manipulation being the most difficult and latest developing of the three skills (Hodson 1994). Finally, pre-schoolers should develop awareness of grapheme-phoneme relationships. By five to seven years of age, children should be able to recognize and blend onsets and rimes and also to segment, blend, and manipulate phonemes. They should have developed grapheme-phoneme correspondence (Hodson 2002).

Pre-Kindergarten	Five- to Seven-Year-Olds
Rhyming	Onsets and rimes Blending
Alliteration	Phonemes Segmentation Blending Manipulation
Words/Syllables Segmentation Blending Manipulation	Grapheme-Phoneme Correspondence
Grapheme-Phoneme Awareness	

Support for the sequence described on the previous pages may be found in a study by Chafouleas et al. (1997). They assessed children's abilities on 11 phonological awareness tasks:

1. *Rhyme-Providing*: ability to provide a rhyming word when a target word is presented orally

2. *Rhyme-Categorization*: ability to determine which of four words does not rhyme

3. *Sound-Providing (alliteration)*: ability to identify the initial, final, or medial sound in a word

4. *Sound-Categorization (alliteration)*: ability to identify which of four words does not have the same initial, final, or medial sound

5. *Blending (phonemes)*: ability to combine phonemes into a word

6. *Segmentation-Counting*: ability to count the number of phonemes in a word using manipulatives

7. *Segmentation-Naming*: ability to state the number of sounds in a target word

8. *Manipulation-Initial deletion*: ability to delete the initial sound from a word

9. *Manipulation-Final deletion*: ability to delete the final phoneme from a word

10. *Manipulation-Substitution*: ability to change the initial, final, or medial sound in a target word to another sound

11. *Manipulation-Reversal*: ability to reverse sounds in a target word (e.g., if given "bat," the child would say "tab")

The study revealed a "small distribution in age between the easiest tasks and the most difficult tasks" (Chafouleas et al. 1997, p. 343). All of the tasks had a median attainment within the six year age range, although mastery for some tasks did not occur until after age six. All of the phonological awareness tasks measured in this study leveled off by age seven, which the researchers attributed primarily to mastery. The acquisition rate for each task varied with tasks such as categorization, substitution, and reversal having longer ranges or greater variability.

These findings indicate that critical aspects of early phonological awareness develop in a short period of time (from preschool to age seven) and in a sequence that can be used to plan instructional activities. Smith (1998) suggested that the first five skills usually emerge in kindergarten whereas the last six usually emerge in first grade.

How does early phonological development impact literacy development?

Based on her research with parent-child book experiences as well as other research, van Kleeck (1998) proposed that preliterate children progress through two stages of development. From birth to three or four years of age, their print experiences focus on the meaning in print. At around three or four years, a transition occurs in which an emphasis on print form and early print form correspondences is added to the print experiences.

Print meaning and print form develop sequentially but separately during the preschool years. Eventually the meaning and form experiences become integrated. ". . . preliteracy [is viewed] as moving from an emphasis on the 'whole' and later to the 'parts,' whereas early reading is viewed as embarking on getting back to the 'whole' but this time independently" (van Kleeck 1998, p. 48). It is during the "parts" period that separate attention must be given to phonological awareness activities in order to call attention to print form.

> Van Kleeck's studies with mother and child book interactions revealed that with infants and toddlers, mothers emphasize the meaning of print, but around three years, and even more at four years, they begin to also direct their child's attention to form aspects of print (1998).

With regard to instruction in preschool and the early grades, van Kleeck (1998) advocated emphasizing print meaning first and then print form. Once print form is introduced, it should be done "explicitly and systematically" (p. 38) in activities that are separated from those emphasizing the meaning of entire narratives. These activities should stress letter knowledge and phonemic awareness.

> With regard to the whole language/phonics debate, van Kleeck cautioned "against 'throwing the baby out with the bath water. . . . The 'baby' of the whole-language movement consists of the meaningful, engaging, child-centered activities it has spawned. The 'bath water,' from my perspective, is that the procedures for dealing with print form advocated by whole language are inadequate for many, though by no means all, children. On the other hand, the 'baby' of the phonics approach is the systematic treatment of aspects of print form (letter knowledge, sound awareness) and early form-meaning correspondences. The 'bath water' in this approach consists of the activities used in phonics programs that assume too much background knowledge (letter knowledge) and hence are too narrow, boring, and out of date" (van Kleeck 1998, p. 49).

What then can we expect children to be doing with regard to reading, spelling, and phonological awareness during the critical period from preschool through first grade?

The following charts indicate behaviors likely to be found at each age level. They are based on information gathered from the following sources:

◆ Snow, Scarborough, and Burns (1999)

◆ California Department of Education (1996)

◆ Hall and Moats (1999)

◆ Snow, Burns, and Griffin (1998)

◆ Hodson (1994)

Three- and Four-Year-Olds

Show interest in books.

Show interest in print on signs and labels.

Recognize some signs and labels.

Recognize some books by their covers.

Know titles of some books.

Look at print and pictures in books.

Know that the print is what you read.

Know to read from front to back and left to right.

Begin to appreciate and repeat rhymes.

Begin to count syllables (50% of children by age four).

Pay attention to repeated sounds in rhymes (e.g., "Peter Peter Pumpkin Eater").

Segment onsets and rimes but not phonemes.

Know alphabet letters have names.

Know some letter names and can identify 10 letters, especially those in their own names.

Experiment with writing by scribbling and writing strings of letters, or letter-like and number-like forms.

Make drawings, scribbles, and letters to make notes and stories.

String letters randomly without regard for sound-letter correspondences.

May write left to right, right to left, or up, down, and backwards.

Begin to use invented or creative spellings with initial consonants.

Kindergartners

Know the parts of a book and their functions.

Begin to track print when listening to a familiar story.

Begin to "read" graphic designs by attending to first and last letters and their sounds.

May read a few short regularly spelled words and may know some sight words.

Know some book titles and authors.

Read their own names and some classmates' names.

Recognize word family patterns.

Demonstrate phonemic awareness for:

   ◆ Rhyming (given a word, can produce a rhyming word)
   ◆ Clapping/counting syllables (90% of children by age five)
   ◆ Substituting sounds
   ◆ Blending phonemes (given sounds, can blend them into a word)
   ◆ Counting phonemes (50% of children by age five)
   ◆ Manipulating letters to make new words (can change *cat* to *hat*)

Separate onsets and rimes with singleton initial consonants.

Attend to word beginnings and endings (e.g., *c-at*)

Begin to figure out the alphabetic system; understand that letter sequences of letters (graphemes) represent sound sequences (phonemes).

Know some letter-sound associations.

Know names and shapes of alphabet letters; recognize and name all uppercase and lowercase letters.

Understand that spoken words consist of sequences of phonemes.

Tell which of three words is different (e.g., *sit, sit, suit*).

Tell which of three words shares a common sound (e.g., *dog, doll, pen*).

Write many uppercase and lowercase letters.

Use phonemic awareness and letter knowledge to spell (invented or creative spelling).

Know some conventionally spelled words.

Write their own names and first names of some friends or classmates.

Write most letters and some words from dictation.

First Graders

Make a transition from emergent to "real" reading.

Read regularly spelled words accurately.

Read somewhat automatically.

Recognize basic word families and patterns.

Accurately decode orthographically regular, one-syllable words and nonsense words.

Use knowledge of letter-sound correspondence to sound out unknown words.

Recognize common irregularly spelled words by sight (e.g., *said*, *two*).

Recognize 50 high frequency words automatically.

Count the number of syllables in a word.

Count phonemes (70% of children by age six).

Divide words by onset and rime.

Blend and segment sounds in one-syllable words.

Manipulate sounds/letters in words (substitute, delete, and reverse).

Match initial consonants.

Identify all letter names and shapes.

Know basic letter-sound correspondences.

Learn the alphabetic code in school.

Attend to and use letter-sound relations to spell.

Use knowledge of consonants, short vowels, and silent -*e* in spelling.

Use conventional spelling for simple regularly spelled words.

Use phonetic spelling to invented spellings when necessary.

Begin to look for word parts and affixes.

Spell familiar and high frequency words.

Chapter 3

What factors are associated with reading and spelling disabilities?

The relationship between phonological awareness and reading and spelling disabilities is critical. This chapter begins with definitions of reading and spelling disabilities. Next, the relationship between language disorders and reading and spelling disabilities is described. In particular, phonological processing, of which phonological awareness is a component, is reviewed. Finally, other factors related to reading and spelling disabilities are addressed.

What are reading and spelling disabilities?

The term **reading disabilities** is often used to refer to children who are having difficulty reading. Because it is a generic term, however, it does little to differentiate specific types of reading problems. **Dyslexia** is a term applied to reading disabilities that is somewhat more definitive. Below are examples of definitions that have evolved as more and more research has emerged that reflects a language component to reading disorders. Note that difficulty with language, and in particular phonological processing, the umbrella term that encompasses phonological awareness, is often inherent within the definitions.

The International Dyslexia Association

The Research Committee of the Orton Dyslexia Society (now the International Dyslexia Association) has adopted a definition of dyslexia that is also used by the National Institute of Child Health and Development (NICHD) (International Dyslexia Association 2002).

> "Dyslexia is one of several distinct learning disabilities. It is a specific **language-based** disorder of constitutional origin, characterized by difficulties in single-word decoding, usually reflecting insufficient **phonological processing** abilities. These difficulties in single-word decoding are often unexpected in relation to age and other cognitive and academic abilities; they are not the result of generalized developmental disability or sensory impairment. Dyslexia is manifested by variable difficulty with different forms of language, often including, in addition to reading problems, a conspicuous problem with acquiring proficiency in writing and spelling" (Lyon 1996, p. 34).

Note: Boldface type is used for emphasis in the definitions. It is not used in the original works.

National Center for Learning Disabilities

When the National Center for Learning Disabilities (NCLD) addresses reading problems, it is again within the context of learning disabilities.

> "Learning disabilities are neurological disorders that interfere with a person's ability to store, process, or produce information, and create a 'gap' between one's ability and performance. Individuals with learning disabilities are generally of average or above-average intelligence" (NCLD 2002, p. 1).

Dyslexia, described as "perhaps the most commonly known learning disability," is the term "used to describe difficulty with **language processing** and its impact on reading, writing, and spelling" (NCLD 2002, p. 1).

Catts and Kamhi Classification

Researchers as well as professional groups have attempted to define dyslexia. Catts and Kamhi (1999a) differentiated reading problems by using the term **dyslexia** to refer only to developmental reading problems as opposed to reading problems associated with language disorders.

> "**Dyslexia** is a **developmental language disorder** whose defining characteristic is difficulty in **phonological processing**. This disorder, which is often genetically transmitted, is generally present at birth and persists throughout the lifespan. Phonological processing difficulties include problems storing, retrieving, and using phonological codes in memory as well as deficits in phonological awareness and speech production. A prominent characteristic of the disorder in school-age children is difficulties learning to decode and spell printed words. These difficulties, in turn, often lead to deficits in reading comprehension and writing" (Catts & Kamhi 1999a, pp. 63-64).

Because approximately one-half of children with reading problems also have other language problems, Catts and Kamhi (1999a) identified a second group of children. These children are referred to as **language learning disabled** (LLD). In addition to **phonological processing** problems, they "may have limitations in vocabulary, morphology, syntax, and/or text-level processing (e.g., narrative comprehension)" (p. 65).

> Catts and Kamhi (1999a) identified a third group of children with language problems associated with reading. They have **hyperlexia**, a disorder characterized by good word recognition abilities but poor listening comprehension. Because this disorder does not involve problems with word recognition (decoding), it will not be addressed in this book.

As can be seen in the preceding definitions, difficulty with spelling is inherent in all the definitions of reading disabilities described (except **hyperlexia**) because spelling, too, is affected when problems with phonological processing occur.

How are language disorders related to reading and spelling disabilities?

While these definitions vary, all of them identify the presence of language problems that have a negative impact on reading and spelling. As is obvious in the definitions, "literacy problems have their foundations in spoken-language difficulties" (ASHA 2001b, p. 25).

In the 1970s and 1980s, language-based theories of reading gained credence because a significant body of literature revealed the impact of language on reading and spelling (Catts & Kamhi, 1999b). Initially, the clinical records of children diagnosed at an early age with spoken language problems who later were diagnosed with reading problems were studied to determine if there was a link between early language disorders and subsequent reading problems. More recently, longitudinal studies have been conducted, enabling researchers to assess language functioning at the preschool or kindergarten levels and then to compare results with reading functioning in the early grades. In addition, the language functioning of poor readers has been studied. Research consistently reveals the impact of language on reading and spelling.

We have chosen to separate research findings that relate to language disorders into two sections. Results related to phonology are summarized in the first section. The second section includes results related to semantics, syntax, morphology, and narrative development.

Phonology

Research has revealed that deficits in phonological processing may impact beginning reading and spelling. As indicated in Chapter 1, phonological processing involves at least four major components or skills: phonological awareness, phonological production, phonological retrieval, and phonological memory.

◆ *Phonological Awareness*

A child's knowledge of phonological awareness on entering school is widely accepted as the single most important predictor of success with reading (Adams & Bruck 1995, Magnusson & Naucler 1990). Children who are aware of the sounds of speech appear to acquire sound-letter correspondence knowledge and use this knowledge to decode printed words. Those who lack an awareness of the sounds contained in words will have difficulty associating sounds with letters (Adams & Bruck 1995, Beck & Juel 1995).

The ability to associate sounds (phonemes) with letters is complex because of the difficulty of accessing speech sounds. Speech is not composed of individual sounds with one said right after another; speech is not segmented. Instead, one sound is merged with another, a phenomenon known as *co-articulation* (Shriberg & Kent 1995). As a result of the merging, sounds are modified; the specific modifications that impact each sound are dependent on the sounds that surround it.

> Say the words *key* and *could*, paying attention to how you say the /k/. Note how the phonemes (sounds) that surround the /k/ affect the way it is produced.
>
> The /k/ in *key* is more forward than the /k/ in *could* because of the influence of the vowels that follow them.
>
> Note also that the phonemes are not produced separately, but are connected together as one.

Because it is difficult to achieve an awareness of the individual segments of speech in words—an ability that is necessary for sounds to be associated with letters (graphemes)—reading may be impacted.

Problems encoding phonological information make letter-to-sound correspondence difficult as well (Jenkins & Bowen 1994). If there are not stable associations between printed letters and the speech sounds associated with them, spelling too will be impacted (Jenkins & Bowen 1994).

Strong relationships between performance on phonological awareness tasks in preschool and kindergarten and later reading achievement have been identified repeatedly (Badian 1994; Catts 1993; Felton 1992; Wagner, Torgesen, & Rashotte 1994; MacDonald & Cornwall 1995). Likewise, linkages between phonological awareness and spelling performance have been reported (Clarke-Klein 1991). In fact, 11 years after the phonological awareness abilities of kindergartners were assessed in a sound deletion task, results continued to be a significant predictor of word identification and spelling skills (MacDonald & Cornwall 1995).

Research has identified areas of phonological awareness and, in particular, phonemic awareness, that are particularly significant.

- Preschoolers as well as illiterate adults had difficulty performing tasks that require segmenting words into phonemes (Morais, Cary, Alegria, & Bertelson 1979; Morais, Bertelson, Cary, & Alegria 1986; Read & Ruyter 1985).

- Poor readers performed less well on phoneme and syllable segmentation tasks than good readers (Blachman 1984, Fox & Routh 1980).

- When results from an assessment of phonological abilities were later compared to reading ability, there was no correlation between ability to perform three rhyming tasks in kindergarten and first grade reading performance. Instead, reading performance in first grade was related to the seven non-rhyming tasks that were assessed and, in fact, correlated more strongly with first grade reading than did a standardized intelligence test. These seven non-rhyming tests were highly interrelated, indicating that they "were tapping a similar construct" (Stanovich, Cunningham & Cramer 1984, p. 187).

- The phonological awareness skills of sound deletion, sound categorization, sound blending, and syllable segmentation were identified as effective in the identification of children in need of early intervention (Swank & Catts 1994).

It is clear that the development of phonological awareness skills is critical to reading and spelling development. In particular, "without phonemic awareness, phonics can make no sense, and the spelling of words can be learned only by rote" (California Department of Education 1996, p. 4).

When children enter school, they demonstrate a wide range of abilities in the area of phonological awareness. By the time they enter first grade, individual differences are even more substantial. According to Torgesen (1995), there are two factors that appear to account for variation, "preschool linguistic experience and genetic endowment" (p. 12).

Preschool linguistic experience

Children who enter school having had experience with nursery rhymes and those who have been exposed to letters, letter sounds, and reading are more advanced in their phonological awareness skills than those who have not. Often, differences correlate with socioeconomic background (Torgesen 1995).

After children enter school, growth in phonological awareness is often related to how they are taught to read as well as their response to reading. Those with explicit knowledge in phonics will become even more aware of the phonological structure of the language, and, if they respond well to instruction, will continue to experience rapid growth (Torgesen 1995).

Genetic endowment

The ability to process phonological information, a component of language, is "strongly heritable" (Torgesen 1995, p. 12). While it appears to be related to general intellectual ability, it is possible to be "average" or "above average" in intelligence and still have significant problems with phonological processing.

It appears, then, that "phonological awareness is both a cause and a consequence of early reading difficulties" (Torgesen 1995, p. 13). Children who are sensitive to phonology as they begin to learn to read will learn quite easily while those without that sensitivity will not develop the more advanced phonological skills that will enable them to profit from early reading instruction (Torgesen 1995).

◆ Phonological Production

Because of the relationship between print and the sounds of language, researchers have studied expressive phonological functioning of children to determine if there is a relationship between problems with phonological production and reading and spelling disabilities. Before discussing results of some of the research that has been done, it is important to differentiate speech sound production problems associated with articulation from those problems associated with phonological production.

If problems with sound production are caused by sensory, structural, or neuromotor deficits, these are articulation problems (Justice, Invernizzi, & Meier 2002). If problems with sound production exist because the rules associated with the phonological system are not known, these are phonological production problems. Rather than involving the motor act of speaking (articulation), these phonological production problems are linguistic.

Research has revealed that, generally, children with articulation problems are not at risk for reading problems (Justice et al. 2002). This is not necessarily the case when speech sound production problems are language-based. Some findings follow.

- The majority of children with expressive phonological disorders had significant problems with reading when assessed at 7 ½ years of age, approximately two years following an initial assessment. Problems appeared linked to difficulty with the alphabetic stage of acquisition, learning the correspondence between graphemes and phonemes. Problems with spelling were also present (Bird, Bishop, & Freeman 1995).

- Children with more severe phonological production problems are at greater risk for reading problems than those with more moderate phonological production problems (Bird et al. 1995).

- When children with expressive phonological disorders were separated into good readers and poor readers, the poor readers had more severe expressive phonological disorders, poorer language skills, and poorer phonological awareness (Larrivee & Catts 1999).

- Children with histories of severe speech-sound deficiencies had more phonological deviations in their spelling errors (Clarke-Klein 1991; Webster & Plante 1992).

- Children with reading and spelling difficulties often had trouble producing phonologically complex words and phrases (Catts 1989, Snowling 1981).

Research has indicated that children with severe phonological disorders are at risk for reading disabilities when they begin school (Bird et al. 1995). While researchers are continuing to study the impact of speech production on reading, it appears that "weak phonological representations affect both speech and language processing and production in children with reading disabilities" (Lombardino et al. 1997, p. 72). Efficient phonological coding in working memory appears to be impacted (Jenkins & Bowen 1994), possibly because of difficulty using subvocal speech rehearsal to maintain phonologically coded information (Webster & Plante 1992). For example, children who delete final sounds may have difficulty with segmentation tasks because they are not aware of the final sound in those tasks (Jenkins & Bowen 1994).

◆ *Phonological Retrieval*

After clinical research revealed that some children who had difficulty reading had word-finding problems, researchers followed up these observations by conducting studies that involved rapid naming tasks. Typically, children were asked to say the names of nonmeaningful groups of letters, numbers, or familiar objects as quickly as possible. While some researchers refer to phonological retrieval tasks as **rapid naming**, others have used the terms **confrontation picture naming** or **continuous naming tasks**. A significant body of research has emerged, attempting to determine the relationship of children's abilities to easily access phonological information that has been stored in long-term memory and reading. Results of a few of the studies follow.

- Poor readers performed more poorly than good readers on tasks involving rapid naming (Katz 1986; Vellutino, Scanlon, & Spearing 1995).

- Poor readers in second grade were four to five times more likely to have problems in phonological awareness and rapid automatized naming as kindergartners than were second graders who were good readers (Catts et al. 1999).

- Deficits in phonological awareness and rapid naming abilities often preceded and were closely associated with problems recognizing words (Bradley & Bryant 1985). It has been determined, however, that phonological awareness and rapid automatized naming appear to contribute somewhat independently to differences in word recognition ability (Blachman 1984; Felton & Brown 1990; Wagner et al. 1987).

- Rapid naming of colors and production of rhymes were significant predictors of reading achievement in kindergarten, while rapid naming of letters, rapid naming of colors, and phoneme segmentation abilities were significant predictors of reading ability in first grade (Blachman 1984).

- When phonological awareness, phonological retrieval (rapid naming), and phonological memory were assessed in children judged to be at risk for reading disabilities while they were in kindergarten and again in first grade, phonological retrieval (rapid naming) was the best predictor of word identification (Felton & Brown, 1990).

After studying the relationship between rapid naming and reading, a number of researchers concluded that rapid naming ability was one of the best predictors of word recognition ability in young children (Badian 1994; Blachman 1984; Felton & Brown 1990; Wolf, Bally, & Morris 1986). It is possible that the efficiency with which individual children name items is related to the rate at which they can access the phonological codes associated with those names from long-term memory. This skill may impact the extent to which phonological information associated with phonemes, syllables, and words is useful in decoding (Baddeley 1986). If deficits in rapid naming co-occur with deficits in phonological awareness, reading will be more affected than if only one or the other processing area is deficient (Wagner, Torgesen, & Rashotte 1999).

◆ *Phonological Memory*

Phonological memory refers to the encoding and storage of phonological information in memory. To determine if there is a link between reading and verbal memory, memory span tasks involving strings of verbal items such as words, digits, or letters have been given to children with and without problems reading. In the past, these tests have been referred to as *tests of memory span*. Researchers have studied the relationship between performance on memory tasks and reading ability. Results from some of the studies follow.

- Poor readers did not perform as well as good readers on verbal memory tasks (Rapala & Brady 1990, Stone & Brady 1995).

- Performance on memory tasks in kindergarten was predictive of reading achievement in the primary grades (Mann & Liberman 1984).

- When phonological awareness, phonological retrieval (rapid naming), and phonological memory were assessed in children judged to be at risk for reading disabilities while they were in kindergarten and again in first grade, a combination of verbal short-term memory and phonological awareness was the best predictor of word attack (Felton & Brown 1990).

- Children with severe reading disabilities had problems using phonologically-based codes to store verbal information (Cohen & Netley 1981, Torgesen 1985).

> Interestingly, studies typically have found no differences between good and poor readers when stimuli are nonverbal and cannot be coded phonologically (Katz, Shankweiler, & Liberman 1981; Rapala & Brady 1990).

Difficulty with memory has been cited as one of the most frequently reported cognitive characteristics of children with severe reading problems (Torgesen et al. 1994), yet, memory has been said to be less consistently associated with reading than other phonological tasks, such as phonological awareness and rapid naming (Stone & Brady 1995).

Some researchers have noted, however, that measures of phonological memory do not account for variability in reading achievement independent of measures of phonological awareness (Wagner et al. 1987). Stone and Brady (1995) suggested that the correlation between phonological memory and phonological awareness may relate to learning to read differently at different stages, with this correlation possibly present only during the early stages of reading development.

It is possible that poor readers have difficulty with short-term recall of spoken or printed information because of problems using phonologically-based codes to store verbal information (Catts & Kamhi 1986). If problems with the mental representation of phonological information are present, it is possible that any task requiring the simultaneous storage and processing of individual sounds in words may be difficult. As such, tasks like blending sounds together to make a word and comparing sounds in different words with one another could be affected (Torgesen et al. 1994).

Wagner, Torgesen, and Rashotte (1999) suggested that phonological coding in short-term memory may not be important for decoding known words, but it may be important when decoding new words. In particular, it may be important when decoding long words.

Assessment tasks involving repetition of sentences may provide additional diagnostic information. During repetition, if the meaning of the sentence is retained but grammatical information is reduced, the errors may be syntactic or morphologic. If only the first or last part of a sentence is recalled, a deficiency in phonological coding in working memory may be present (Swank 1994).

Semantics, Syntax, Morphology, and Narrative Development

Research has revealed language areas other than phonology that also impact reading and spelling. Results obtained from a few studies follow.

◆ Children with reading comprehension problems performed poorer than good readers on tests assessing semantic ability (Nation & Snowling 1998).

◆ Children with reading problems often had difficulty with listening comprehension (Smiley et al. 1977).

◆ When children in second grade were designated as poor readers or good readers on the basis of reading performance, poor readers were more likely to have had problems with oral language ability involving vocabulary, grammar, and narration as kindergartners than were good readers. (Catts et al. 1999).

◆ Some children with language disorders in the areas of syntax and language comprehension prior to kindergarten had difficulty reading and spelling in first grade (Magnusson & Naucler 1990).

◆ Deficiencies in measures of sentence length and grammatical complexity at 2 ½ years of age were related to difficulties reading in second grade (Scarborough 1990).

◆ When children with speech-language disorders were given a series of language tests, standardized measures of semantic-syntactic abilities accounted for more individual differences in reading comprehension than did tests of phonological awareness and rapid naming (Catts 1993).

◆ Not all spelling errors reflect phonological processing deficits. Some reflect use of nonstandard orthographic forms and thus have been described as lexical in nature (Clarke-Klein 1994).

◆ Children who perform poorly on measures of syntax may be at risk for reading problems (Menyuk et al. 1991).

◆ Children who had early language difficulties at age four but whose problems had resolved by age five, were not at risk for literacy problems. Those who still had language impairment at 5 ½ years were more likely to have reading and spelling difficulties (Bishop & Adams 1990). The researchers suggested that these problems "occur in the context of persisting deficits in comprehension and expression of spoken language" and may impact reading comprehension to a greater extent than decoding (p. 1046). It is possible, they claimed, that children's comprehension problems may be overlooked because of their reading and spelling accuracy.

Research has clearly demonstrated that children diagnosed with spoken language impairments in preschool or kindergarten are at risk (Aram, Ekelman, & Nation 1984; Bishop & Adams 1990; Menyuk et al. 1991). Even if children enter school having resolved language deficits in all areas but one, they continue to be at risk (Justice et al. 2002).

> It is important to remember, however, that not all children with spoken language disorders will achieve lower reading levels than those without spoken language disorders (Magnusson & Naucler 1990).

If language disorders are present, it appears that phonological deficits as well as deficits in semantics, grammar, and narration are most problematic (Catts 1993; Catts et al. 1999; Nation & Snowling 1998; Menyuk et al. 1991; Scarborough 1990).

Researchers have not only revealed a link between language functioning and reading, but additionally they have hypothesized that difficulty reading may also impact continued development of spoken language. Poor readers have fewer opportunities to acquire linguistic knowledge through reading because they do not read (Donahue 1984; Guthrie et al. 1999). Because children further develop vocabulary, syntax, and a knowledge of text-level structures through reading, the inability to read may impact continued development of these language structures (American Speech-Language-Hearing Association 2001b).

What other factors might be associated with reading and spelling disabilities?

Other factors might also be associated with literacy disabilities. Snow, Burns, and Griffin (1998) separated factors into those involving groups and those involving individuals.

Group Factors

Children may be at risk for reading problems because of one or more of the following group conditions:

◆ They attend a school where achievement is chronically low.

◆ They live in low-income families within poor neighborhoods.

◆ They have limited English proficiency.

◆ They speak in a dialect significantly different from the one used in school.

Individual Factors

Children may be at risk because of one or more of the following individual conditions:

◆ They have parents with a history of reading problems.

◆ They acquired less literacy knowledge or skill during the preschool years either because of cognitive limitations or a lack of home literacy experiences.

◆ They have a hearing impairment.

◆ They have a primary medical diagnosis with which reading problems often occur as a secondary symptom (e.g., Down syndrome).

Snow et al. (1998) also include children diagnosed as having early language deficits and those who have below age level skills in "literacy-related cognitive-linguistic processing, especially phonological awareness, confrontational naming, sentence/story recall, and general language ability" (p. 132), areas addressed in greater detail earlier in this chapter.

Summary

According to the *Simple View of Reading* theory (Hoover & Gough 1990), reading comprehension consists of word recognition (decoding) and listening comprehension. Phonological processing deficits (problems with phonological awareness, phonological memory, phonological retrieval, and phonological production) are more likely to impact decoding, whereas pragmatic and textlinguistic deficits seem more likely to impact listening comprehension. Semantic and syntactic deficits seem likely to impact both listening comprehension and decoding.

The impact of oral language deficits on reading is significant. When Catts et al. (1999) studied reading performance of second graders and compared it with oral language abilities as kindergartners, they found that "deficits in oral language were as common in poor readers as were deficits in phonological processing" (p. 342). They emphasized that, while critical, phonological skills do not "supercede other language abilities in explaining many aspects of early reading achievement . . ."(p. 353). Instead, both phonological skills and oral language ability "are essential in predicting early reading achievement" (p. 353).

Phonological skills that may impact reading involve awareness, production, retrieval, and memory.

◆ Phonological awareness deficits seem to be particularly problematic for children learning to read and spell. In fact, it is widely accepted as the single most important predictor of success with reading (Adams & Bruck 1995, Magnusson & Naucler 1990).

◆ Children with more severe phonological production problems may be especially at risk for phonological awareness deficits (Bird et al. 1995), perhaps because of difficulty using subvocal speech rehearsal to maintain phonologically coded information (Webster & Plante 1992).

◆ Phonological awareness and phonological retrieval problems appear to function independently (Blachman 1984, Felton & Brown 1990, Wagner et al. 1987). The efficiency with which children name items may be related to the rate at which they can access the phonological codes associated with those names from long-term memory (Baddeley 1986).

◆ Memory and phonological awareness are closely intertwined (Wagner et al. 1987). Poor readers may have difficulty with short-term recall of spoken or printed information because of problems using phonological codes to store verbal information (Catts & Kamhi 1986).

While the focus of this chapter has been on the impact of language on reading and spelling, it is important to remember that other factors may also impact early literacy. These factors may be environmental, experiential, and biological (Snow et al. 1998). It is clear that learning to read and spell is a complex, multidimensional process. Many factors are involved, any of which can impact literacy.

Chapter 4

How is phonological awareness assessed?

The goal of reading is to comprehend text. Two abilities are required for good reading comprehension: the ability to comprehend language and the ability to identify words in print accurately and fluently (Torgesen 1998).

The development of phonological awareness is critical to the development of word recognition. The term **phonological awareness** is a more general level of awareness than is phonemic awareness. For example, phonological awareness includes knowledge of rhyming and the ability to segment words into syllables as well as the more advanced tasks often differentiated by the term **phonemic awareness**. Phonemic awareness is used to describe that advanced level of phonological awareness—the ability to manipulate individual phonemes within words. Deleting the first sound of words or determining whether two words begin with the same sound would be classified as phonemic awareness tasks. Performance on these phonemic awareness tasks is predictive of individual differences in reading growth (Lundberg, Frost, & Peterson 1988).

This chapter first addresses general considerations regarding assessment. Then specific tools for assessing phonological awareness, phonological processing, phonological retrieval, and phonological memory are reviewed. The chapter concludes by considering other language areas that might be assessed.

Why do the more difficult phonological awareness tasks—those involving phonemic awareness—appear to make such significant contributions to early reading?

Torgesen (1999) stated that there are at least three ways in which phonemic awareness contributes to early reading skills.

1. "It helps children understand the alphabetic principle" (p. 130). Children must be aware that when reading English, an alphabetic language, words contain sound segments that are represented by letters in print. With this knowledge, they understand why "sounding out" words is critical to the reading process.

2. "It helps children notice the regular ways that letters represent sounds in words" (p. 130). Children will notice how letters correspond to sounds if they hear that there are three sounds in the word *dog* and four in the word *snap*. Torgesen stated that the awareness of the relationship of sounds to spelling has two benefits. "First, it reinforces knowledge of

individual sound-letter correspondences, and second, it helps in forming mental representations of words that involve a close amalgamation of their written and spoken forms" (p. 130).

3. "It makes it possible to generate possibilities for words in context that are only partially 'sounded out'" (p. 130). A child who can read the first words in a sentence but can only recognize the beginning sound in the last word can use that ability "to search the lexicon for words that begin with similar sounds" (p. 130). For example, if the child can read the first five words and the first sound of the sixth as indicated in the following sentence, "He wanted to ride his b _ _ _," he may be able to figure out the last word using a combination of phonemic awareness and context.

Development of decoding skills is critical to the reading process. "There is no way that beginners can attain mature levels of reading and writing without acquiring knowledge of the alphabetic system and utilizing this to build a vocabulary of sight words" (Ehri 1998, pp. 32-33). It is through development of decoding skills that readers develop the ability to read words automatically, "the key to skilled reading of text" (Ehri 1998, p. 11).

What types of tasks have researchers used to measure phonemic awareness in words?

According to Catts et al. (as cited in Torgesen 1999), three broad categories of tasks have been used to measure awareness of phonemes in words: phoneme segmentation, phoneme synthesis, and sound comparison.

Phoneme segmentation tasks require a relatively explicit level of awareness of phonemes because they involve counting, pronouncing, deleting, adding, or reversing the individual phonemes in words. Examples "require pronouncing the individual phonemes in words ("Say the sounds in *cat* one at a time."), deleting sounds from words ("Say *card* without saying the /d/ sound.") or counting sounds ("Put one marker on the line for each sound you hear in the word *fast*.")" (Torgesen 1999, p. 133).

Phoneme synthesis is a sound blending task in which a series of phonemes in isolation is pronounced and a child is asked to blend them together to form a word ("What word do these sounds make, /f/ - /æ/ - /t/?" *fat*) (Torgesen 1999, p. 133).

Sound comparison tasks involve making comparisons between the sounds in different words. For example, a child might be asked to indicate which word (of several) begins or ends with the same sound as a target word. Additionally, tasks that require children to generate words that have the same first, last, or middle sound as a target word would fall in this category (Torgesen 1999).

Torgesen (1999) suggested that phonemic awareness tasks all appear to measure essentially the "same construct" (p. 133) even though some are more difficult than others. Variance may be due to the amount of explicit phoneme manipulation necessary to complete a task. For example, while phoneme segmentation tasks are difficult for most children in kindergarten, many of them can complete sound comparison tasks (Torgesen 1999).

If the more difficult phonemic tasks appear more predictive of individual differences in reading growth than the easier phonological awareness tasks, why assess the easier tasks?

Rhyming

While most children can detect rhymes and produce them without any type of formal instruction, Adams et al. (1998) stated that rhyming appears to be a relatively simple, entry level phonological awareness task. Can a child attend to the sounds of words rather than their meanings so as to appreciate the similarity that exists between words such as *ball* and *call*? While success may not be directly related to phonemic awareness, poor functioning may warrant intervention (Adams et al. 1998).

Counting Syllables

Research indicates that counting syllables within words is easier than counting phonemes (Lundberg et al. 1988). Adams et al. (1998) included syllable counting in an informal assessment they developed, noting that it is a precursor to the development of phonemic awareness.

Why should phonological awareness be assessed?

Rationales for assessing phonological awareness may differ. Assessment may be undertaken for the following reasons:

◆ to identify where to begin instruction prior to using a curriculum in a classroom and, subsequently, to monitor progress (Adams et al. 1998)

◆ to identify children at risk for reading failure before instruction has begun (Torgesen 1999)

◆ to determine the degree of phonological impairment that may exist in children who are having difficulty reading (Torgesen 1999)

When should phonological awareness tests be administered?

If the purpose of an assessment is to identify children at risk for reading problems, it is suggested that children not be assessed during the first semester of kindergarten. Because children have widely diverse preschool learning opportunities, many children may be identified as at risk when, in actuality, they have not yet had the opportunity to learn skills. If prereading skills are "actively taught" in kindergarten, screening could be administered during the second semester (Torgesen 1998, p. 35).

Is it possible to predict which children are at risk for reading failure based on assessment results?

If the purpose of an assessment is to identify children for preventive instruction, it is important to realize that the "ability to predict which children will have the most serious reading problems is still far from perfect" (Torgesen 1998, p. 35).

◆ False positive errors are made when children are identified as at risk but later turn out to be good readers.

◆ False negative errors are made when children are not identified as at risk but later turn out to have reading problems.

If the intent of an assessment is to maximize the chances of identifying as many children as possible at an early age, it is suggested that a cut-off be set that may over-identify rather than under-identify. Even though some of the children may not be the most seriously disabled readers at a later age, most will likely to be below average readers (Torgesen & Burgess 1998, pp. 161-189).

Is it necessary to administer a nationally standardized test?

Torgesen (1998) suggested that, while more definitive information is possible using national norms, it is not necessary to administer such a test in order to identify children at risk for reading problems. If a nationally standardized test is not administered, however, professionals involved with assessment should determine appropriate standards for the population of children they serve.

Should only phonological awareness be assessed?

Because it is widely believed that a child's level of phonological awareness is the single most important predictor of the success a child will have in learning to read (Adams 1990, Stanovich 1986), it is critical that phonological awareness be assessed.

However, because research has revealed that children with a history of speech-language problems are at risk for developing reading problems, Catts et al. (2001) suggested that areas other than phonological awareness should also be assessed. In particular, they suggested that letter identification, sentence imitation, and rapid naming should be assessed because of the predictive value of these areas. Information about a mother's educational background may be gathered as it, too, has proven to be predictive.

When should these other areas be assessed?

Because children with a history of speech-language problems are at risk for developing reading problems, these areas should be assessed as early as possible during the kindergarten year (Catts et al. 2001).

To identify children who do not have a history of speech-language problems but may be at risk for difficulty reading, kindergarten teachers should make referrals to the speech-language pathologist as well as to the reading specialist. According to Catts et al. (2001), children with any of the following characteristics should be referred:

◆ appear behind in their familiarity with books

◆ appear behind in speech-language development

◆ cannot perform the phonological awareness tasks generally found in a kindergarten curriculum (e.g., rhyming).

Is screening for possible problems appropriate or should children be given a battery of tests?

There are a number of reasons why a screening assessment may be more appropriate than a battery of tests.

◆ Some states have mandated that all children entering school be screened to determine if they are at risk for literacy problems (Justice, Invernizzi, & Meier 2002).

◆ Using screening assessments may be more efficient than administering full test batteries (Justice, Invernizzi, & Meier 2002). Results can be used to determine those children who may require additional assessment and intervention.

◆ If the purpose of an assessment is to obtain baseline data prior to beginning a preventive program, screening may be appropriate.

◆ If the purpose is to separate children who are at risk from those who are not, screening may be the most efficient way to accomplish this. Results can then be used to decide if further assessment and intervention is indicated.

While Torgesen (1998) cautioned that batteries of tests are better at predicting than single tests, he suggested that two types of tests could be administered if efficiency is desired:

◆ a test of letter knowledge or sounds, as letter knowledge continues to be the best single predictor of reading difficulties

◆ a test of phonemic awareness (most predictive for first grade children) to provide additional predictive information.

Torgesen (1998) also suggested that information about attention, motivation, and home background should be supplemented with teacher ratings of behavior and attention.

According to Justice et al. (2002), a screening protocol should include "areas of performance relating most significantly to literacy outcomes" (p. 88). They suggested administration of a screening tool that assesses early literacy in six general categories, each contributing "in unique although independent ways to literacy achievement" (p. 88):

◆ written language awareness

◆ phonological awareness

◆ letter name knowledge

◆ grapheme-phoneme correspondence

◆ literacy motivation

◆ home literacy

(See Appendix B, page 122, for more specific information.)

As noted earlier, however, there may be a rationale for obtaining standardized test results or for obtaining a significant body of information. By all means, then, use assessment tools that will enable you to obtain the results needed. For example, children with a history of oral language problems when they enter school are at risk for reading problems. Not all of these children, however, will have been identified at the onset of kindergarten. If additional testing is needed to obtain a more in-depth understanding of already diagnosed problems or to obtain data to verify or rule out suspected problems, a more complete battery of tests should be administered.

If a full battery of tests is desired, what should be included?

Recently, a position statement of the American Speech-Language-Hearing Association (ASHA) (2001b) developed by members of the Ad Hoc Committee on Reading and Written Language Disorders, was disseminated to speech-language pathologists.

Included in the accompanying guidelines (ASHA 2001a) were formal and informal assessment activities appropriate at specific developmental grade levels. Components, supported by research, were organized in three stages. Those activities included within two of the stages, emergent and early, follow:

◆ **Emergent (preschool)**

Family literacy
Phonological awareness (syllables and rhymes)
Print awareness
Spoken language
  Phonology
  Lexical semantics
  Sentence-level syntax, morphology, and semantics
  Narrative discourse
        (ASHA 2001a, pp. 9-10)

◆ **Early (kindergarten to third grade)**
  (specific tasks within areas may vary depending on grade level)

Phonological awareness
Rapid naming
Phonological memory
Letter identification
Invented spelling
Reading
        (ASHA 2001a, pp. 10-11)

Why should invented spelling be assessed?

Invented spelling, a form of phonemic awareness, has been found to identify kindergarten children who may be at risk for reading problems (Lombardino et al. 1997). Assessment of invented spelling during the first six weeks in first grade has been found to be one of the best predictors of at risk readers at the end of first grade (Gilbertson & Bramlett 1998). According to Lombardino et al. (1997), invented spelling can be easily assessed. A word of caution is in order, however. Gilbertson and Bramlett (1998) found that the test of invented spelling used during their research identified many readers who were not at risk for reading problems. It is suggested, therefore, that a battery of tests should be administered, not just a test of invented spelling, before concluding that a child is at risk for reading problems.

What questions should be answered prior to choosing assessment tools?

The choice of assessment tools will vary depending on the purpose of the assessment. The following questions should be answered.

- ◆ What is the purpose of the assessment?

- ◆ Should only phonological awareness be assessed or should phonological processing be assessed as well?

- ◆ Should other speech-language components be assessed?

- ◆ Will a group of children or an individual child be assessed?

- ◆ Are the assessment tools being considered culturally and linguistically appropriate?

- ◆ Are the assessment activities being considered developmentally appropriate?

- ◆ Are normative data desired? If so, were norms developed on children who match the children considered for the assessment?

- ◆ Are the assessment tools being considered reliable and valid?

What tools could be used to assess those areas found to impact reading and spelling?

A cross-section of tools that may be used to assess phonological awareness is provided on pages 57-61. While language areas other than phonological processing also impact reading and spelling, a review of tools used to assess these areas is beyond the scope of this book. If there are concerns about semantic, syntactic, morphological, pragmatic, or narrative deficits, a speech-language pathologist should evaluate the child.

What about other phonological processing areas?

We have also included some suggestions for assessment tools that have been developed to assess phonological production, phonological retrieval, and phonological memory, the other phonological processing areas (pages 61-64).

How is the information about assessment tools organized?

A short description of each assessment tool is included along with the following information:

◆ information about which phonological processing area(s) is assessed

◆ where the assessment tool can be located

◆ if the tool is designed for individual or group administration

◆ whether the tool is standardized

◆ if the tool assesses additional areas that also may impact literacy acquisition

Is the information summarized?

A chart is provided on page 65 that lists each assessment tool mentioned and indicates which phonological processing area(s) is assessed using that tool. It also indicates if other areas that may impact literacy acquisition can be assessed using the tool.

Assessment of Phonological Awareness

Knowledge of phonological awareness is widely accepted as the single most important predictor of success with reading (Adams & Bruck 1995; Magnusson & Naucler 1990; Stanovich, Cunningham, & Cramer 1984; Wagner & Torgesen 1987). Without phonemic awareness, the component of phonological awareness that involves the manipulation of speech sounds, phonics makes no sense and spelling can be learned only through rote memorization (California Department of Education 1996).

We have divided the assessment tools that may be used to assess phonological awareness into three sections.

◆ The first section contains specific information about screening tools that can be used to determine if further evaluation is indicated.

◆ The second section contains two articles that may be helpful in planning an assessment of invented spelling, a form of phonemic awareness.

◆ The third section contains a cross-section of tools developed to assess phonological awareness.

Screening Tools

There are two screening tools that we felt should be included in this book.

◆ Catts (1997) developed a checklist to identify children who are at risk for reading disabilities before experiencing failure. The checklist can be used to determine whether an in-depth assessment is needed. (See Appendix A, page 120.)

◆ Suggestions and examples of tasks that could be designed for screening early literacy are included in a chart developed by Justice, Invernizzi, and Meier (2002). Professionals involved with early literacy could design a tool appropriate for their setting using this information. Then, results could be used to determine if more intensive evaluation is needed. (See Appendix B, page 122.)

Invented Spelling Articles

There are two articles you may want to read if you are considering assessing invented spelling.

◆ Lombardino, Bedford, et al. (1997) described a protocol they used to assess invented spelling of second semester kindergartners. They suggested that evaluating the acquisition of basic phonic skills identifies children who may be at risk for reading problems.

◆ Clarke-Klein (1994) developed a protocol for children with phonological production problems using phonological processes to evaluate invented spelling. This information as well as treatment procedures are provided in the article.

Informal and Formal Tests

◆ *The Assessment Test*

Authors: Marilyn Jager Adams, Barbara R. Foorman, Ingvar Lundberg,
      and Terri Beeler (1998)
Publisher: Paul H. Brookes Publishing Co.

Group administration
   Kindergartners in groups of two or three or, if necessary, no more than six
   First graders in groups no larger than 15
Not standardized
   Suggestions provided for interpretation of results
Grades kindergarten through first

According to the authors, this tool may be used to assess a classroom of children prior to introducing a curriculum designed to enhance phonological awareness and subsequently, to monitor progress. Subtests that assess rhymes, syllables, words, phonemes, and phoneme-grapheme correspondence are included. The assessment is in the book *Phonemic Awareness in Young Children: A Classroom Curriculum* (Adams et al. 1998).

◆ *Comprehensive Test of Phonological Processing (CTOPP)*

Authors: Richard Wagner, Joseph Torgesen, and Carol Rashotte (1999)
Publisher: PRO-ED

Individual administration
Standardized
Ages
   Version one: ages 5 and 6 (primarily kindergartners and first graders)
   Version two: ages 7 through 24 years (primarily second graders through college)

The *CTOPP* assesses phonological awareness, phonological memory, and rapid naming. It was designed to identify children who are significantly weaker than their peers in phonological abilities, to determine specific strengths and weaknesses, to document progress as a consequence of intervention, and to be used as a measurement tool in research. A Phonological Awareness Quotient may be obtained using scores from the phonological awareness subtests.

◆ *Lindamood Auditory Conceptualization Test*

Authors: Charles H. Lindamood & Patricia C. Lindamood (1971)
Publisher: The Psychological Corporation

Individual administration
Criterion referenced
Ages preschool through adult

The *Lindamood Auditory Conceptualization Test* was designed to measure auditory perception and conceptualization of speech sounds. The test assesses the ability to discriminate one speech sound from another and to separate a word into its phonemes.

◆ *Phonological Abilities Test*

Authors: Valerie Muter, Charles Hulme, and Margaret Snowling (1997)
Publisher: The Psychological Corporation

Individual administration
Standardized
Ages 5 through 7; normative data also for 4-year-olds.

The *Phonological Abilities Test* was designed to identify children at risk for reading difficulties. It assesses phonological awareness, speech rate, and letter knowledge.

◆ *Test of Phonological Awareness (TOPA)*

Authors: Joseph K. Torgesen and Brian R. Bryant (1994b)
Publisher: The Psychological Corporation

Individual or group administration
Standardized
Ages 5 through 8 years

The *TOPA* was designed to assess children's awareness of the individual sounds in words. There are two versions, one designed for kindergarten children that involves comparisons of the initial sounds in words and a second version for first and second graders that involves comparison of the final sounds of words.

◆ *The Phonological Awareness Profile*

Authors: Carolyn Robertson and Wanda Salter (1995b)
Publisher: LinguiSystems

Individual administration
Criterion referenced
Grades kindergarten through third

The Phonological Awareness Profile was designed to assess pre-reading and writing skills. Phonological awareness skills assessed include rhyming; blending sounds; identifying sounds; segmenting syllables, words, and syllables; and substituting and deleting sounds. Sound-symbol relationships can also be assessed through tasks such as decoding nonsense words and invented spelling.

◆ *The Phonological Awareness Test*

Authors: Carolyn Robertson and Wanda Salter (1997)
Publisher: LinguiSystems

Individual administration
Standardized with computerized scoring available
Grades kindergarten through third

The Phonological Awareness Test was designed to determine why a student has difficulty reading or writing, the hierarchy of phonological awareness skill development, a child's developmental age for each skill, and how a child compares to a group of children identified as at risk for reading. Subtests involve rhyming, segmentation, isolating sounds, deleting, substituting, blending, grapheme, and decoding. Results provide suggestions as to whether intervention is necessary and if so, where teaching should begin. Home and classroom suggestions are also provided.

◆ *The Predictive Reading Profile (PRP)*

Author: Jane Flynn Anderson (2001)
Publisher: LinguiSystems

Individual or group administration
Designed to set up local norms; preliminary comparison norms provided
Grades kindergarten through first

The PRP was designed as a screening tool to assess the phonological, orthographic, visual-spatial, semantic, and syntactic processes crucial for success in reading. It is typically administered at the end of kindergarten or the beginning of first grade to identify children at risk for reading failure and to identify special instructional needs in literacy. Subtests involving logographic/sight word knowledge, sound recognition, syllable and sound counting, visual matching, vocabulary, and syntax are also included. Optional subtests involve story writing and phoneme segmentation.

....

Assessment of Other Phonological Processing Areas

....

Research has revealed that phonological processing areas other than phonological awareness also impact literacy (Bird, Bishop, & Freeman 1995; Catts et al. 1999; Katz 1986; Mann & Liberman 1984; Rapala & Brady 1990; Torgesen 1995). Tests have been developed specifically to assess these areas; a sampling of these has been provided. In addition, we've included phonological awareness tests that include subtests assessing these other phonological processing areas.

Phonological Production

Research has revealed that when children with severe phonological disorders begin school, they are at risk for reading disabilities (Bird et al. 1995). A speech-language pathologist should see any children having significant difficulties with speech sound production. Consideration could be given to administration of one of the following tests.

◆ *Assessment of Phonological Processes—Revised (APP-R)*

Author: Barbara Williams Hodson (1986)
Publisher: The Psychological Corporation

Individual administration
Criterion referenced
Grades preschool and school-aged

The *APP-R* was designed to provide the speech-language pathologist with an efficient diagnostic tool in order to develop individualized remediation programs for children with severe to profound speech disorders. Descriptions of over 30 phonological processes are provided. The *APP-R* also includes an assessment of multisyllabic word production designed for the older elementary-school child who appears less intelligible in conversation. Both screening and diagnostic assessments are available.

◆ *Bankson-Bernthal Test of Phonology (BBTOP)*

Authors: Nicholas W. Bankson and John E. Bernthal (1999)
Publisher: The Psychological Corporation

Individual administration
Standardized
Ages 3 through 9

The *BBTOP* was developed to probe 10 of the most frequently occurring phonological processes. Normed scores from one or all three inventories may be determined—Word Inventory, Consonant Inventory, or Phonological Process Inventory.

◆ *Khan-Lewis Phonological Analysis, Second Edition (KLPA-2)*

Authors: Linda Khan & Nancy Lewis (2002)
Publisher: American Guidance Service

Individual administration
Standardized
Ages 2 to 21

The Sounds-in-Words section of *The Goldman-Fristoe Test of Articulation—2* (Goldman & Fristoe 2000) is administered in phonological notation. Then responses are transferred to the *KLPA-2* Analysis Form and scored. Results can be used not only to diagnose but also to plan remediation for 15 common phonological disorders.

Phonological Retrieval (Rapid Naming)

Rapid naming ability has proven to be one of the best predictors of word recognition ability in young children (Badian 1994; Blachman 1984; Felton & Brown 1990; Wolf, Bally, & Morris 1986). This skill may impact the extent to which phonological awareness is useful in decoding (Wagner, Torgesen, & Rashotte 1999). In particular, reading fluency is impacted. If children have deficits in both rapid naming and phonological awareness, they are at greater risk than if they had deficits in one or the other of these areas (Wagner, Torgesen, & Rashotte, 1999). Consideration should be given to assessment of this skill.

◆ *Comprehensive Test of Phonological Processing (CTOPP)*

Authors: Richard Wagner, Joseph K. Torgesen, and Carol Rashotte (1999)
Publisher: PRO-ED

Individual administration
Standardized
Ages: Version one for ages 5 and 6 (primarily kindergartners and first graders)
　　　　Version two for ages 7 through 24 years (primarily second graders
　　　　through college)

(See a more complete description of *CTOPP* on pages 58-59.) Rapid naming subtests may be combined to obtain a Rapid Naming Quotient.

◆ *Test of Word Finding—Second Edition (TWF-2)*

Author: Diane German (2000)
Publisher: PRO-ED

Individual administration
Standardized
Ages 4 through 12

The Test of Word Finding—Second Edition, consists of two components. The first component is a standardized assessment which includes procedures for computing a Word Finding Quotient based on a student's accuracy and speed when retrieving single words. The second component is an informal assessment which consists of five supplemental analyses to further probe word finding abilities. Three forms are provided: a pre-primary form for preschool and kindergarten children, a primary form for first and second grade children, and an intermediate form for third through sixth grade children.

Phonological Memory

Children with reading problems, as well as those who are at risk for developing them, often have difficulty with verbal short-term memory (Mann & Liberman 1984, Torgesen 1985). They have difficulty following directions, taking messages, or learning to pronounce new words (Catts 1996). While some children have difficulty on tests of memory span, such as remembering digits, others have difficulty remembering sentences.

Memory may be affected because of problems using phonologically-based codes to store verbal information (Catts & Kamhi 1986). In particular, deficits in short-term memory may make decoding of especially long unfamiliar words difficult (Wagner, Torgesen, & Rashotte 1999).

Consideration should be given to assessment of memory. When analyzing results, it is important to remember the following if a sentence repetition task is used. If only the first or last part of a sentence is recalled, a deficit in phonological coding in working memory may be present. If the meaning components of a sentence are recalled but grammatical information is reduced, the errors may be syntactic or morphologic (Swank 1994).

◆ *Comprehensive Test of Phonological Processing (CTOPP)*

Authors: Richard Wagner, Joseph K. Torgesen, and Carol Rashotte (1999)
Publisher: PRO-ED

Individual administration
Standardized
Ages: Version one for ages 5 and 6 (primarily kindergartners and first graders)
Version two for ages 7 through 24 years (primarily second graders through college)

(See a more complete description of *CTOPP* on pages 58-59.) Administration of phonological memory subtests may be combined to obtain a Phonological Memory Quotient.

Summary of Informal and Formal Assessment Tools

The following chart provides information about the phonological processing areas assessed in the tools described. "Other" indicates that the assessment tool includes other areas found to impact literacy development. Tools are listed in the order in which they were mentioned in the text.

Name of Test	PA	PP	PR	PM	Other
The Assessment Test	X				
Comprehensive Test of Phonological Processing	X		X	X	
Lindamood Auditory ConceptualizationTest	X				
Phonological Abilities Test	X				X
Test of Phonological Awareness	X				
The Phonological Awareness Profile	X				X
The Phonological Awareness Test	X				
The Predictive Reading Profile	X				X
Assessment of Phonological Processes—Revised		X			
Bankson-Bernthal Test of Phonology		X			
Khan-Lewis Phonological Analysis, Second Edition		X			
Test of Word Finding—Second Edition			X		

PA = phonological awareness
PP = phonological production
PR = phonological retrieval
PM = phonological memory
Other = subtests in other language areas

Chapter 5

How are phonological awareness skills developed?

Based on what we know about the importance of phonological awareness to normal reading and spelling development, it seems reasonable to include activities to stimulate phonological awareness in preschool and early grade curricula. Research has shown that phonological awareness can be developed with direct training (Lundberg, Frost & Peterson 1988) and, when combined with instruction in grapheme-phoneme correspondences, can impact early reading development (Bradley and Bryant 1985).

This chapter presents suggestions for activities to increase phonological awareness in children from preschool (ages 3-4 years) through first grade (ages 6-7 years). The activities are organized in five categories:

◆ Preparatory Activities

◆ Rhyme Awareness Activities

◆ Sound Awareness Activities

◆ Segmenting and Blending Activities

◆ Manipulation Activities

Who should receive phonological awareness intervention?

We believe all preschool, kindergarten, and first grade children should receive phonological awareness instruction. Children with language disorders, children with phonological production disorders, or children at risk for reading and spelling disabilities should receive additional instruction in phonological awareness.

How are the activities organized?

Throughout the chapter, activities and the materials needed are described. The categories targeted are presented in a developmental order; activities within each category generally progress from easier to harder. Some activities for preschoolers, however, may be appropriate for slower maturing kindergartners; similarly, some activities for first graders may be appropriate for mature kindergartners. Many of the activities are also appropriate for older children for whom individual intervention is needed.

How should the activities be presented?

Activities should be playful. Avoid drills and rote memorization. Typically, introduce the activities into classroom or small group activities. Include culturally diverse materials and consider any cultural variations in sound production. (If questions or concerns about cultural variations arise, secure assistance from the family, cultural informants, bilingual professionals, or translators). Include 10 to 15 minutes of direct phonological awareness activities each day, and incorporate phonological awareness activities into many classroom activities.

How should sounds be introduced?

Focus first on the sounds in these activities and then the letters. Likewise, help the children become "meta" by helping them focus on the *sounds* of language, not just their meaning. For example, when introducing sounds, help the children to attend to what is happening in their mouths when they say the sounds. Encourage them to tell where they make the sounds (e.g., in the front or back of the mouth), whether there is voicing (e.g., by feeling their throats), and if the sound is long or short (e.g., /m/ versus /b/). Encourage the children to compare sounds with each other. Finally, encourage children to think about what happens when sounds change in words. For example, when talking about the words *mat* and *cat*, you could help the children see that the words are different in the following ways:

◆ the first sound in each word is different

◆ /m/ is a long sound, but /k/ is a short sound

◆ /m/ has voicing, but /k/ does not

◆ /m/ is made in the front of the mouth with the lips, but /k/ is made in the back of the mouth with the tongue

◆ the words *mat* and *cat* mean two different things

> **Voiced sounds**: vowels and all consonants except /p, t, k, f, ʃ (sh), h, tʃ (ch), θ (voiceless th)/
> **Front sounds**: /b, p, m, w, f, v, ð (voiced th)/
> **Middle sounds**: /t, d, n, s, z, r, ʃ (sh), ʒ (zh), j (y), tʃ (ch), dʒ (j)/
> **Back sounds**: /k, g, ŋ (ng), h/
> **Stops** (short sounds): /p, b, t, d, k, g/
> **Continuants** (long sounds): vowels and all other consonants except /tʃ (ch)/ and /dʒ (j)/ which are affricates, a combination of a stop and continuant

Similarly, when introducing work on beginning, middle, and ending sounds, talk about what these terms mean and how they relate to words. Help children compare how parts of words stay the same and how they change by providing examples. Talking about "parts" or "little bits" of words will help children realize that words are made of separate sounds. Providing visual (e.g., printed letters), tactile (e.g., touching a block for each sound), and movement (e.g., clapping for each syllable or sound) cues will also help children begin to recognize the individual sounds in the stream of connected speech and their relationship to letters in print.

How should graphemes be introduced?

Introduce written words and letters when appropriate to help children begin to make associations between phonemes and graphemes. For young children (pre-kindergarten and early kindergarten), though, the presence of printed letters may be distracting or confusing, especially if the children have not yet been introduced to the alphabet. Use your own judgment to determine when the children are ready for graphemes in the activities.

Typically, for preschool children, focus on sound awareness. Appropriate work would be learning the alphabet song and doing letter puzzles. By kindergarten, introduce both sounds and graphemes. By first grade, consistently integrate sound-letter (phoneme-grapheme) correspondences into phonological awareness activities. Also encourage children to print the graphemes whenever possible. Help them recognize and think about word patterns and point out how to apply their knowledge of phoneme-grapheme correspondences and patterns to new words.

What happens if children have difficulty with the tasks?

Most young children have a natural curiosity about language. We can capitalize on this by responding positively and enthusiastically to their attempts to manipulate words and sounds. Young children vary a great deal, however, in their abilities to respond to phonological awareness activities. Activities need to be fun and informal so that children continue to participate and grow even when they are not as adept as some of their classmates.

What if a child seems to have trouble remembering the directions or does not respond to questions?

First, rephrase the directions. If this does not help, increase the use of visual, tactile, and motor cues. If you think the child knows the response but cannot retrieve the word, sound, or letter name, offer a choice (e.g., "Is it *L* or *P*?" or "Does it start with a /k/ or /f/ sound?").

What if a child has speech (sound production) or language problems?

A speech-language pathologist needs to see the child. Children with significant phonological production problems should not only receive phonological therapy, but they should also have additional work on phonological awareness incorporated into their phonological therapy. Children with language disorders often have phonological awareness deficits and may need individual or small group therapy in addition to the classroom activities described in this chapter. As SLPs, we routinely include a phonological awareness goal in therapy for preschool children with language disorders enrolled in our clinic. Recently, we have also begun incorporating a phonological awareness goal into therapy for preschool children with phonological production disorders.

Preparatory Activities

Since phonological awareness activities require children to listen to the sounds of language, it is important to be sure that they have good listening skills before introducing these activities. This first section includes activities designed to focus the children's attention on developing good listening habits and then on listening for sounds in general, as a prerequisite for listening to speech sounds.

Engage in Listening Activities: Preschool—Early Kindergarten

◆ Sing the Listening Song below to the tune of "Pop Goes the Weasel" to get ready for Listening Time.

"Let's sit down—it's Listening Time.
We'll watch, be quiet, and listen.
We'll use our ears for Listening Time.
Shh! It's time to listen."

◆ Listen to tapes of animal, vehicle, or environmental sounds and identify the sounds. Talk about the importance of sounds and how they communicate information to us. Have the children close their eyes while listening so that they focus on the sounds, not other visual distractions. (If tapes are not available, make your own sounds for the children to identify.)

◆ Present a sequence of two or three animal, vehicle, or environmental sounds. Have the children tell what they heard in the order in which the sounds were presented.

◆ Present a sequence of three animal, vehicle, or environmental sounds. Then repeat the sequence but omit one sound. Have the children tell which sound was missing.

◆ Play listening games, such as "Simon Says."

Engage in Sound Play: Preschool—Early Kindergarten

Young children need to play with sounds. **Rhyming** is a good place to begin. Children between three and four enjoy books with rhymes and often will create rhymes themselves. Rhyming activities draw children's attention to the sounds in words. Children must focus on how rhyming words sound rather than what they mean. Rhymes also help children begin to recognize that words have parts (i.e., beginnings and endings) and that these parts can be the same or different. Bryant, Bradley, Maclean, & Crossland (1989) found that children who had had experiences with rhymes as toddlers (three-year-olds) had better phonological awareness skills as four- to six-year-olds.

> ". . . gaining full meaning is somewhat beside the point in rhyming books. The point is the playful *sound* of language, and children who tune into the sound of language have an easier transition to learning an alphabetic writing system that relies on phonological awareness" (van Kleeck 1998, p. 44).

Listening for and responding to **rhythm** are also important as rhythm provides a base from which to recognize the syllable structure of English. Activities that help children respond to rhythm in general can be used to lead them into recognizing rhythm (i.e., syllables) in speech; therefore, activities related to rhythm are also included in this section on sound play.

Finally, young children can recognize rhythm in words by identifying their syllables. Fox and Routh (1975) found that three-year-olds could **segment syllables** in familiar words about half the time and that four-year-olds could do it for all the words provided in their study. This section ends with suggestions for syllable segmenting.

◆ *Rhymes*

- Have the children listen to and recite nursery rhymes and finger plays. Talk about the rhyming words (i.e., how they sound the same). Recite the rhymes, leaving off the rhyming word and wait expectantly for the children to fill it in. Talk about how the ends of the words are the same, which makes them rhyme.

- Sing songs and recite TV jingles. Talk about the rhyming words.

- Read stories with lots of rhymes (e.g., *Brown Bear, Brown Bear, What Do You See?* by Bill Martin Jr). Talk about the rhymes. Repeat the rhyming lines, leaving off the rhyming word and wait expectantly for the children to fill it in.

- Play circle games with rhymes. Have the children stand in a circle; go around the circle reciting the "One potato, two potatoes" rhyme. Tap on each child's shoulder as you recite the words. The children who are the rhyming words (e.g., *four* and *more*) have to sit down. Continue repeating the rhyme until only one child is left. Be sure to repeat the rhyming words and talk about how they rhyme. The following rhymes are also good for this type of game:

  I'm a Little Teapot   Hickory Dickory Dock
  Pease Porridge Hot   Eensy Weensy Spider

- Sing sound-play songs, such as "Apples and Bananas" from *Raffi in Concert with the Rise and Shine Band* (Raffi 1989); oldies, such as "DooWah Diddy Diddy" from *The Sixties TV Sound Tape* (Mann 1999) and "The Name Game" (*More Silly Songs*, 1998); or children's favorites, such as "Old MacDonald," "This Old Man," and "B-I-N-G-O."

- Encourage children to engage in sound play by adding endings to words (e.g., *mouthie, handie, footie*). Sometimes the first word may be the only real word (e.g., *jumbo, tumbo, lumbo, dumbo* or *panda, manda, fanda, randa*).

- Recite this rhyme and then repeat it changing the sounds: "Hey, He, Hi, Ho, Hoo. I can say this rhyme. How about you?" When you repeat the rhyme, change the beginning sound (e.g., "Say, See, Sigh, So, Sue. I can say this rhyme. How about you?"). You can also have the children put the sound at the beginning of their name into the rhyme. Another variation involves a greeting—"Bay Bee Bye Bo Boo. I am Barbara. Who are you?" You can change the sound to match the beginning sound of the child's name (e.g., "Say See Sigh So Sue. I am Sarah. Who are you?")

> To prepare the children for later phoneme-grapheme relations, you can show the letter most commonly associated with the sounds, but be sure to emphasize the sound first and then the letter (e.g., "Let's put the /s/ sound at the beginning of our rhyme. The letter *S* makes that sound." If introducing letters seems to confuse the children, omit the letters and focus on the sounds.

◆ Rhythm Play

- Play circle games with sound play, such as "Eenie, meenie, minie, mo."

- Have children use musical instruments (e.g., drum sticks or tambourines) to tap out the rhythm to songs. If instruments are not available, simply clap a pattern and have the children imitate the pattern.

◆ Syllable Play

- Have the children clap out the syllables in their names. This is also a good time to talk about long versus short words. Some children will have long names and some short; some children will have long names but short nicknames (Alexander/Alex) and vice versa (James/Jimmy).

- Encourage the children to listen for syllables in words. Have them clap their hands or jump for the number of syllables. Incorporate words being taught in curricular units. Some examples of one-, two-, and three-syllable words in preschool units are listed below:

One syllable	Two syllables	Three syllables
Food		
peach	apple	banana
pear	carrot	broccoli
plum	raisin	tomato
lime	pepper	lasagna
peas	cherry	spaghetti
pop	soda	strawberry
corn	milk shake	pineapple
grape	popcorn	hamburger
Vehicles		
car	airplane	snowmobile
truck	skateboard	bulldozer
van	tractor	bicycle
sled	canoe	
ship	tugboat	
train	wagon	

School

book	pencil	principal
tape	chalkboard	telephone
desk	playground	computer
flag	backpack	
nurse	teacher	
bell	paper	

Home

desk	sofa	wallpaper
bed	table	apartment
chair	window	dishwasher
clock	ceiling	piano
fork	oven	spatula
stove	attic	teakettle
knife	bathtub	
spoon	shower	
sink	bedroom	
house	garage	
couch	dresser	

Clothes

coat	sandals	pajamas
shirt	raincoat	umbrella
blouse	mitten	underwear
glove	bathrobe	overcoat
skirt	sweatshirt	

Animals

cat	goldfish	butterfly
dog	raccoon	dragonfly
pig	tiger	elephant
fish	lizard	kangaroo
fox	donkey	crocodile
bear	spider	dinosaur
snake	penguin	buffalo

People

vet	doctor	principal
nurse	dancer	firefighter
coach	teacher	janitor
clerk	waiter	musician
chef	artist	magician

- When reading books to the children, say some of the words from the book and have the children clap or tap the syllables. For example, from *Brown Bear, Brown Bear, What Do You See?* by Martin (1983), children could clap once for *bear* and *frog* and twice for *goldfish* and *teacher*.

Tune in to Print: Preschool—Kindergarten

Children who learn an alphabetic language such as English need to become familiar with print in general and with the alphabet in particular. Children need to know the names of letters, the shapes of letters, and the sounds of letters. "Because letter knowledge is the anchor for the entire reading 'system,' it behooves preschoolers to solidly learn and even overlearn letters" (van Kleeck 1998, p. 36.). Letter knowledge, however, must be coupled with other preliteracy activities (e.g., phonological awareness activities); therefore, early introduction to letters and then incorporation of letters into phonological awareness activities provides the best approach. Encourage children to name letters as well as say the sounds they make. If they have trouble recalling the letter name, give them a choice (e.g., "Is it *L* or *M*?").

- Tune the children in to print in the environment around them. For example, point out print on their clothes and toys or on other items in the home, school, or community (e.g., posters, billboards, magazines, stop signs).

- Encourage the children to learn "The Alphabet Song."

- Play letter matching games. Print each letter on a sheet of construction paper and post them on the board or wall. Give each child a letter on another sheet of paper with a double-sided piece of tape on the back. Have the child stick the letter on the sheet of paper that matches that letter. For variety, lay the papers with the letters on the floor (perhaps only a few at a time) and have the children match plastic letters or blocks to the letters. Then have the children name the letters. If they have trouble, give them a choice (e.g., "Is it *L* or *P*?").

- Give the children lowercase letters of the alphabet and have them match them to capital letters placed on the board or around the room. Have the children name the letters. If they have trouble, give them a choice (e.g., "Is it *P* or *F*?").

- Talk to the children about the first letter in each of their names. Tell them the sound it makes as well as its name. Have each child find "his or her letter" in other places around the room. Talk about the unusual ones. For example, point out that C can be /k/ as in Carl or /s/ as in Cindy and sometimes one sound requires two letters (e.g., *SH* for Shirley). If children have names with cultural variations in pronunciations, point those out too (e.g., Jorge).

◆ Play "Hide and Seek" with letters hidden around the room. At first only hide three or four different letters. Increase the number of letters as children experience success.

◆ Provide opportunities to play with magnetic letters or blocks with letters. Encourage the children to find "their special letters." Be sure to talk about the sound each letter makes and then the letter's name.

◆ Play "Grocery Store" and talk about foods that start with different sounds. Print the words and point out the beginning letters. Place these words next to toy objects set up like a grocery store. Give each child a letter and have him or her find a food to buy that begins with that letter.

◆ Introduce key words to associate with the letters and sounds (e.g., *A* is for *apple*, *B* is for *bear*).

◆ Give the children letters on construction paper. Tell them you are going to call out a letter and if they have it, they should hold it up or stand up. Say, "Show me an *A*."

◆ Have the children see if they can think of objects that look like the letters (e.g., *U* = smile; *M* = McDonald's).

◆ Read alphabet books to the children like the following:
   Chicka Chicka Boom Boom by Martin (1989)
   Eating the Alphabet: Fruits and Vegetables from A to Z by Ehlert (1989)
   Animal Alphabet by Kitchen (1984)
   My Name Is Alice by Bayer (1984)

◆ Sing along with the songs from Sesame Street: *Sing the Alphabet* (1996).

The following activities are designed primarily for preschool and kindergarten children. They could, however, be used with first graders or with older children who have not yet developed these skills. As indicated earlier, rhyming activities tune children in to the fact that words are composed of parts and that these parts can be the same or different. Rhymes help children develop phonological awareness skills (Bryant, Bradley, Maclean, & Crossland 1989). Rhymes help children begin the transition from focusing only on *meaning* in print to focusing also on the *form* of print.

The Sound Play activities on pages 70-73 focused on *playing* with rhymes. Although children should continue to have these experiences, they also need practice *creating* rhymes and *categorizing* words based on rhyming elements. Activities in this section focus on developing the last two skills.

Rhyme Providing/Creating: Preschool—Kindergarten

◆ Encourage the children to create rhymes with their names. Have them change the first letter/sound of a name to create a rhyme (e.g., "Tom-Pom" or "Suzie-Muzie").

◆ Make a rhyming book for the class with each child's name and rhyming words (they do not all have to be real words, but encourage children to use a variety of initial consonants when creating rhymes).

◆ Recite familiar nursery rhymes or songs and have the children whisper the rhyming words or have them say the rhyming words in a louder voice. Some examples of good rhymes follow:

Hickory Dickory Dock Mary, Mary, Quite Contrary
Twinkle, Twinkle, Little Star Eensy Weensy Spider
I'm a Little Teapot Row, Row, Row Your Boat

◆ Recite familiar rhymes but leave off the rhyming word and have the children fill it in. For example:

"Hickory dickory dock,
The mouse ran up the ____.
The clock struck one,
The mouse ran down.
Hickory dickory ____."

◆ For small groups, play a matching (concentration) game with rhyming pictures.

◆ Play a circle game with rhyming words. Have the children sit in a circle. Using pictures of familiar objects, hold up a picture and have the children raise their hands if they can think of a rhyming word. Give the picture to the first child who can. Since many words might rhyme, continue to allow children to respond even though the picture has been given to the first child to respond. Continue with other pictures.

Rhyme Categorizing: Preschool—Kindergarten

◆ Read books with rhymes. Ask the children to say the rhyming words. Make a list of the rhyming pairs from the book by writing them on the board. Have the children try to think of other words that rhyme with the rhyming pairs.

◆ Introduce Queen Alpha and King Bets and their twins, Princess Tammy and Prince Sammy (See Appendix C, page 123). Tell the children that today is Princess Tammy's and Prince Sammy's birthday. They always get things that are alike for presents. Tell the children that you have to find cards with rhyming words to give them because rhyming words sound alike at the end. Give an example: "The twins want *man* and *pan* because they rhyme, but they don't want *man* and *coat* because they don't rhyme." Say two words from picture cards and ask if they rhyme (e.g., *hat/coat*). If they do, have one child give the cards to Princess Tammy and Prince Sammy; if the words don't rhyme, set the cards aside. For additional practice, see if the children can think of other rhyming words to go with the rhyming pairs. Here are some rhyming and non-rhyming pairs to present. Pictures of the pairs may be found in Appendix C, pages 124-125:

cat/hat	cat/dog
car/jar	car/truck
bed/red	bed/chair
house/mouse	house/garage
sink/rink	sink/stove
lime/dime	lime/pear
mice/rice	mice/birds
lake/rake	lake/river

◆ Name three pictures, one of which does not rhyme. Have the children decide which one does not rhyme.

◆ Name a picture. Then say two more words. Ask the children which word rhymes with the pictured word. Write the rhyming words on the board. To prepare for sound-letter (phoneme-grapheme) relations, print the words so they can see how the words group by letters as well as sounds. When different spellings result, point out these changes to the children (e.g., *-ite* [kite] and *-ight* [light]).

◆ Have the children sit in a circle. Pass out pictures of objects from three different rhyming categories (e.g., *-an*, *-ig*, *-en*). Go around the circle and have each child hold up his or her picture so that you can name it. Then have the child repeat the name. Next hold up a picture from one of the rhyming categories (e.g., man). Name the word and ask the children, "Who has a word that rhymes with *man*?" Have each of the children who raise their hands, say his or her word and, if it rhymes, put the picture in the "*-an*" pile. Repeat the process with other words until you have three piles of rhyming categories. At the end, go through each pile and have the children name the rhyming words. Begin with short vowel words such as those listed below. Pictures can be found in Appendix C, pages 126-127.

-an	-ig	-en	-at	-in	-ot	-ug
man	pig	ten	mat	pin	pot	rug
pan	big	pen	cat	fin	cot	mug
fan	wig	den	bat	win	hot	tug
can	dig	men	rat	chin	dot	bug

For variety, print a rime on the board such as those listed above. Have each child pick a letter (or letter block or plastic letter) and place it in front of the word family and then "read" the word. Some words will be real and some nonsense. Some will sound real but won't be spelled correctly (e.g., *f-o-t* for *fought*). Talk about these unusual spellings. You might even keep a list of words with unusual spellings on the board. Wylie and Durrell (1970) reported that from 37 basic rimes (word families), nearly 500 primary-grade words can be created. We suggest that you introduce these rimes in groups as indicated in the box on the next page. The groups progress from simpler rimes in Group 1 (those with only two sounds and two letters in the rime) to harder ones in Group 6 (those with vowel digraphs, vowel *r*, consonant clusters, consonant digraphs, and unusual spellings).

If selecting words from this list, progress through these groupings:

Group 1: -at, -op, -in, -an, -ap, -ip, -ug
Group 2: -ide, -ate, -oke, -ake, -ale, -ame, -ine, -ice
Group 3: -ack, -ick, -uck
Group 4: -all, -ill, -ell
Group 5: -ank, -ump, -unk, -ink, -ing
Group 6: -eat, -ain, -ir, -ore, -or, -aw, -ay, -ight, -ash, -est

Sound Awareness Activities

One of the most important phonological awareness skills is the ability to identify grapheme-phoneme relationships. Before being able to recognize these relationships, though, children need to become aware of the sounds that occur at the beginning, middle, and end of words. They need to categorize words based on shared sound elements. Developing this ability begins with rhyming as children learn to categorize words by their rhyming elements, but now they need to expand this ability by categorizing words by their sound elements. Children first need to categorize words by the following:

◆ initial sounds

◆ final sounds

◆ medial sounds

Once children can categorize sounds, they can also determine which sounds do not fit into categories (an oddity task). Bradley and Bryant (1985) found "that a child's skill in tests of sound categorization at the time he goes to school plays an important part in his learning to read and to spell" (p. 119). They also found that use of categorization activities reduced the number of phonological awareness problems in a group of pre-schoolers. Additionally, they found "that teaching sound categorization alone to children already at school does have an effect on progress in reading and spelling. But that effect is vastly amplified if the training is accompanied by experience with alphabetic letters. In other words, children who are already being taught to read are helped even more if the sound categories are encapsulated in alphabetic letters too" (Bradley and Bryant 1985, p. 119).

Follow this sequence when working on sound awareness in the initial position:

◆ Begin with continuant sounds, such as /f, v, s, z, m, n, ∫ (sh), θ (th)/ as these sounds can be stretched out, making it easier to focus on them.

◆ After children can hear continuant sounds, introduce voiceless stop consonants (/p, t, k/).

◆ Finally, introduce voiced stop consonants (/b, d, g/).

For stop sounds, consider repeating the initial consonant (e.g., t-t-t-top), but try not to include the "uh" sound when doing so. It is easier to produce voiceless stops without the "uh" than voiced stops which is why it's best to begin with voiceless stops.

> While these techniques are commonly used, some caution is advised. Remember that young children often make sound production errors that may interfere with their abilities to make some of the sounds correctly. Also, some children may demonstrate disfluencies (stuttering-like behaviors) that will be mimicked in these techniques (e.g., sound repetitions and prolongations). Teachers should discuss the use of these techniques with the speech-language pathologist if children with significant sound production or fluency problems are in the class.

Activities in the following section are designed to help children develop the ability to identify initial, medial, and final sounds in words and to group words into categories based on their shared sound elements.

Initial Sounds: Preschool—Kindergarten

◆ Make a sound and have the children think of someone in the class whose name starts with that sound.

◆ Play "Guess Who" with the children's names. Say, "I know someone whose name begins with this sound "SSSSS" (or for stop consonants, D-D-D). Have the children guess all the people who have names beginning with that sound. Write the names on the board so the children can see the letter(s) that goes (go) with the sounds.

◆ Play "I'm thinking of something that begins with the ___ sound." Have the children look around the room and find objects that begin with the targeted sound. Write the words on the board. Point out that they all begin with the same letter (or, if they begin with different letters, point out that more than one letter can make some sounds).

◆ Show the children the pictures from Appendix C, pages 128-129. Name the three pictures and have the children say which two start with the same sound/letter. The words are listed below:

fan	foot	boat
man	moon	cup
vase	coat	van
shoe	ship	duck
pan	saw	sun
seal	soap	bed

◆ Make a sound and have the children think of words that begin with that sound. Begin with continuant sounds, such as /f, v, s, z, m, n, ʃ (sh), θ (voiceless th)/. Then introduce voiceless (/p, t, k/) and finally voiced stops (/b, d, g/).

◆ Sing the following song to the tune of "Twinkle, Twinkle, Little Star." Remember to make the sound, not the letter (e.g., /f/ not *F*).

"What's a word that starts with /f/?
What's a word that starts with /f/?
If you know one, raise your hand.
What's a word that starts with /f/?"

After someone thinks of a word, have everyone join in this verse:

"(Fish) is a word that starts with /f/.
It's a word that starts with /f/.
Give your back a great big pat
For thinking of a word like that!"

Repeat with other sounds. Since the sound is emphasized and not the letter, knowledge of the associated grapheme is not necessary; however, to prepare the children for phoneme-grapheme associations, you might hold up the grapheme most commonly associated with the sound.

◆ Read books or stories that have a lot of alliteration (i.e., same beginning consonants) like *Tikki Tikki Tembo* (Mosel 1968) and *Noisy Nora* (Wells 1997). Talk about the words that start with the same sound.

◆ Say a word and ask the children what sound is at the beginning of the word. Write the word on the board and ask them to think of other words that start with that sound. Group words by letters but be sure to point out the unusual ones (e.g., *C* that is /k/ or /s/; *S* that is /s/ or /ʃ/ [sh]; *G* that is /g/ or /dʒ/ [j]).

◆ Say two words and then ask the children which one begins with the target sound. For example, say "Does *dog* or *cat* begin with the /d/ sound?"

◆ Have the children listen to a word (e.g., *dog*). Then say, "I'm going to say three more words. Tell me which one starts with the same sound as *dog*: *ball, dish, cat*."

◆ Write three letters on separate sheets of construction paper. Hold up each sheet of paper and have the children make the sound that goes with each letter (e.g., *L* = /l/; *M* = /m/). If they cannot remember the sound, give them a choice (e.g., "Does *M* say /m/ or /k/?"). Remember to point out the unusual ones (e.g., *SH* has two letters but makes one sound, but *C* is one letter that makes two different sounds, /k/ and /s/). Then place each letter at a different place in the room. Give each child an object or picture that begins with one of the letters. Have each child name the object or picture and then go stand by the letter that makes the beginning sound in his or her word.

◆ Introduce each sound with a story. Talk about the letter that makes the sound and the words in the story that begin with the sound. Stories are included in Appendix C, pages 130-160). Introduce the stories in the order listed moving across each row:

Silly Sally /s/	Fay Fox /f/	Harvey Hound /h/
Molly Moose /m/	Nurse Nora /n/	Vera Vet /v/
Zippy Zookeeper /z/	Wally Window Washer /w/	Yolanda Yawner /j/ (y)
Luther Lizard /l/	Ruthie Robot /r/	Polly Penguin /p/
Talented Tim /t/	Kathy Kitten /k/	Billy Baboon /b/
Dolly Donkey /d/	Gary Goose /g/	Shirley Sheep /ʃ/ (sh)
Theodore Thinker /θ/ (th)	Cherry Cheetah /tʃ/ (ch)	Jerry Joker /dʒ/ (j)
Adam Actor /æ/ short a	Eddie Egg /ɛ/ short e	Icky Iguana /ɪ/ short i
Ozzie Otter /a/ short o	Uppidy Up /ʌ/ short u	Ada Ape /e/ long a
Ebert Eel /i/ long e	Ida Icicle /aɪ/ long i	Opie Oboe /o/ long o
Ukulele User /ju/ long u		

> The stories have been ordered so that continuant consonant sounds are introduced first, followed by voiceless and then voiced stops, and ending with consonant digraphs (sh, th) and affricates (ch, j). Short vowels are then presented followed by long vowels. Names for vowel characters have been selected to make sure that the vowel is not followed directly by a nasal (m, n) or a liquid (r, l) since these sounds tend to color the vowel, changing the sound.

◆ Give a puppet a name that begins with a sound (e.g., Larry the Lion). Tell the children that the puppet only eats things that start with its sound (e.g., /l/). Give each child two pictures, one that begins with /l/ and one that doesn't. Have the children come up one at a time and feed the puppet the food Larry Lion likes. (Have different puppets for different sounds or have the children make puppets for different sounds.)

◆ Play "Post Office." Tape paper mailboxes on a chart with a letter printed on the front of each mailbox. (See the mailbox pattern in Appendix C, page 161.) Give the children pictures that begin with the sounds made by the letters written on the mailboxes. Have each child name his or her picture and then "mail" it into the proper mailbox by sliding it into the slot. Begin with just two mailboxes. Gradually add more mailboxes as the children learn more sounds.

◆ For small group work, lay out a picture of a word that begins with a sound (e.g., lion for /l/) and another picture for another sound (e.g., soup for /s/). Then show the children pictures that begin with either of the two sounds and have them put them beside the target word that begins with the same sound.

◆ Sing the following song to the tune of "Pop Goes the Weasel":

"What's the sound that starts these words?
What sound is in the beginning?
What's the sound that starts each word?
Tell me what you heard."

Then say these three words: *sock, soup, sun*. When someone says /s/, say "Yes. Now let's sing this verse." Be sure to sing the sound, not the letter.

"/s/ is the sound that starts these words.
/s/ is the sound you heard.
/s/ is the sound that starts the words.
/s/ is what you heard."

Repeat using the sets of words below:

/f/ fish, face, farm	/v/ visit, vet, vest
/z/ zoo, zipper, zero	/w/ wish, watch, wind
/ʃ/ (sh) shoe, ship, shack	/θ/ (th) thick, think, thumb
/m/ mouse, milk, man	/n/ nose, neck, nice
/l/ leaf, lip, leg	/r/ rose, rate, rug
/p/ pie, pig, pen	/t/ top, tape, time
/k/ key, kite, kiss	/b/ ball, bat, bed
/d/ dish, dog, duck	/g/ goat, gate, gum
/tʃ/ (ch) chalk, chin, chair	/dʒ/ (j) jar, joke, jump

◆ Sing songs with lots of alliteration. Talk about the beginning sound. For example, *Singable Songs for the Very Young* (Raffi 1976) has "Robin in the Rain," "Willoughby Wallaby, Woo," "Baa, Baa, Black Sheep," and "Five Little Frogs." "Baby Beluga" in *Raffi in Concert with the Rise and Shine Band* (Raffi 1989) is also good.

◆ Have a sound for the day. Introduce it with a story. (See stories in Appendix C, pages 130-160). Have the children help you think of words that begin with that sound. Then have them draw pictures or paste pictures on a poster with the sound. Give each child a "special name" for the day by substituting the sound for the day for the first sound in his or her name (e.g., "Tom" = "Nom") or if the name begins with a vowel, by adding the sound (e.g., "Alice" = Nalice"). Introduce other activities such as those listed below for each of the sounds. Remember to say the words containing the target sounds frequently.

/s/

Activity 1: Tell the children that you are going to talk about the word *slow*. Ask them which sound is at the beginning of *slow*. Have the children think of things that start with the /s/ sound that they could do in slow motion, such as sliding, sawing, stepping, spinning, stomping, swinging, skating, swimming, sweeping, and skiing. Then have them do the actions.

Activity 2: Give each child a paper sack. Remind them that *sack* starts with the /s/ sound. Tell the children that they are going to make faces on their paper sacks. Each child can choose to draw a silly face, a sad face, or a smiling face. Point out that the words *silly*, *sad*, and *smiling* also start with the /s/ sound.

/f/

Activity 1: Talk about families. Tell the children that the word *family* starts with the /f/ sound. Have them each draw a picture of his or her family and then talk about the picture.

Activity 2: Have the children look at their fingers. Ask them what the first sound is in the word *finger*. Then ask them to name some things that start with the /f/ sound, such as family, a farmer, a fire, a frog, a fish, a fox, flowers, a forest, and food. Finally, have the children finger paint, making something that starts with the /f/ sound.

/h/

Activity 1: Have the children name as many body parts as they can that start with the /h/ sound (e.g., head, heart, hand, hip, heels, hair).

Activity 2: Have the children trace their hands onto a sheet of paper. When the children are done tracing their hands, remind them that the word hand starts with the /h/ sound. Have the children draw faces on each finger and draw different hats on each finger. Have the children talk about their hands and hats. Be sure to point out that the words *hand* and *hat* also start with the /h/ sound.

/m/

Activity 1: Talk about the nursery rhymes "Little Miss Muffet" and "Mary Had a Little Lamb." Explain that Miss Muffet and Mary have the /m/ sound at the beginning of their names. Ask who else has the /m/ sound at the beginning of their names.

Activity 2: Give each child some paper. Tell them that they are going to make a book about themselves called "All About Me." Remind them that the word *me* starts with the /m/ sound. Have the children think about things they like that start with the /m/ sound, such as movies, milk, masks, monkeys, money, the moon, mud, music, mice, magic shows, and mountains. Have them draw some of their favorite things on their papers. When they are finished, help each child fold a sheet of construction paper to make a front and back cover for his or her pictures. Then write "All About Me" on the cover, print his or her name, and staple the pages together.

/ n/

Activity 1: Bring in lots of different kinds of noodles. Ask the children what sound is at the beginning of *noodle*. See if the children can think of other words that start with /n/. Give the children paper with a big "N" printed on it. Then give them noodles and glue and have them glue the noodles onto the "N."

Activity 2: Bring in some things that smell, such as cookies, a rose, a glass of juice, an orange, shampoo, and perfume. Have the children talk about what a nose does. Then ask them what sound the word *nose* starts with. Tell them they are going to play a guessing game with their noses. Show them the objects. Have the children close their eyes. Have them smell an object, guess what it is, and ask what they used to decide (i.e., their noses). Ask them if the object smells "nice." Ask them what sound the word *nice* starts with.

/v/

Activity 1: Tell the children you are going to talk about vacations. The word *vacation* starts with the /v/ sound. Have the children talk about different things they could do on vacation, such as swim, fish, walk, bike, climb mountains, or ski. Ask each child to tell what he or she would like to do on vacation. Each time a child says the word *vacation*, have the other children clap their hands.

Activity 2: Tell the children you are going to talk about vans. Ask them what sound is at the beginning of the word *van*. Have the children talk about where they could go in a van. They might go to a movie, the store, the swimming pool, or a friend's house. Then divide the children into small groups. Tell them each group is riding in a different van. When you say "red light," the vans must stop. When you say "green light," the vans can go. See if the children can move as a group as they travel around the room.

/z/

Activity 1: Make a zigzag line on the chalkboard. Tell the children that it is a zigzag. Then tell the children that *zigzag* means to make quick turns when you are drawing or when you are moving. Next have the children stand in a line. Have each child put his or her hands on the waist of the child in front of him or her. Finally have the children zigzag around the room as they listen to a song.

Activity 2: Talk with the children about different fasteners that keep their clothes together. Some fasteners we use are buttons, zippers, Velcro, snaps, and hooks and eyes. Ask the children which of these fasteners starts with the /z/ sound. *Zipper* starts with the /z/ sound. Then have the children tell what kind of fasteners they have on their clothing. Each time someone says a word that starts with the /z/ sound, have the children pretend to zip up a sweatshirt they are wearing.

/w/

Activity 1: Tell the children you want them to be wiggle worms. For this activity, they can wiggle all they want! Tell them *wiggle* and *worm* start with the /w/ sound. Then have them listen to some music and wiggle around the room to the rhythm.

Activity 2: Tell the children they are going to learn a poem called "Wee Willie Winkie." Ask the children what sound is at the beginning of each word in the title "Wee Willie Winkie." Read the poem. Tell them to wink their eyes whenever they hear a /w/ sound. Point out that *wink* also starts with /w/.

> "Wee Willie Winkie runs through the town,
> Upstairs and downstairs, in his nightgown,
> Rapping at the window, crying through the lock,
> 'Are the children in their beds?
> Now it's eight o'clock.' "

/j/ (y)

Activity 1: Tell the children that you are going to talk about yards. The word *yard* starts with the /j/ (y) sound. Have the children take turns telling what they have in their yards, saying something like, "I have a swing set in my yard" or "Our yard has a fence around it." Have the children clap their hands each time they hear a /j/ (y) sound at the beginning of a word.

Activity 2: Give each child a sheet of paper. Tell the children that you are going to talk about things that are yellow. Ask them what sound the word *yellow* starts with. Then have the children name as many yellow objects as they can. They might name the sun, corn, flowers, a pear, a lemon, a duckling, an apple, lemonade, butter, or leaves. Then have each child draw a picture of something he or she likes that's yellow. When the children are finished, have them tell what they made, saying something like, "I drew a yellow ball" or "I made a picture of a yellow house." Have the children stand up each time they hear a word that starts with the /j/ (y) sound.

/l/

Activity 1: Have the children make paper lollipops. Mention that *lollipop* starts with the /l/ sound. Also talk about what kinds of lollipops they "like" and how they "lick" lollipops. Point out that the words *like* and *lick* both start with the /l/ sound.

Activity 2: Sing the counting song, but use the word *lion* as follows:

"One little, two little, three little lions,
Four little, five little, six little lions,
Seven little, eight little, nine little lions,
Ten little lions roaring!"

Ask the children what sound is at the beginning of the words *lion* and *little*.

/r/

Activity 1: Put some objects that start with /r/ at the end of the room in two piles (e.g., a rope, ruler, ring, ribbon, rocket, rug, rock, and rabbit). Divide the class into two groups. Tell them you are going to have a relay race with /r/ words. Remind them that the words *relay* and *race* both start with the /r/ sound. Have the first child in each group run up and pick one of the /r/ objects and then run back and give it to the next child. That child then runs up, puts down that object, and picks up the next /r/ object. Continue until both groups are done. Name the objects and ask the children to tell you what sound they all start with. Congratulate the children on all being good "runners."

Activity 2: Sing "Row, Row, Row Your Boat." Have the children pretend to row a boat. Ask them what sound is at the beginning of the word *row*.

/p/

Activity 1: Tell the children the word *pet* starts with the /p/ sound. Have the children talk about their pets or the kinds of pets they would like to have. See how many pets they can think of that start with the /p/ sound, such as a parrot, puppy, pig, possum, pony, peacock, pigeon, parakeet, pelican, poodle, and a porpoise.

Activity 2: Tell the children you are going to talk about objects that are "pink" and "purple." Ask them to think of things that are pink or purple. If the object starts with a /p/ sound, write its name on the chalkboard (e.g., pink pig). Some examples of pink and/or purple things are listed below:

paint	pill	plum
pen	pan	pie
petunia	pompom	pencil

/t/

Activity 1: Get out a tape recorder. Ask the children what we do with a tape recorder (i.e., talk into it). Remind the children that the words *tape recorder* and *talk* both start with the /t/ sound. Have each child "talk" into the recorder by saying his or her name. Then tell them each to think of a word that starts with /t/ and say it into the recorder.

Activity 2: Give the children some clay or play dough. Tell them to think of something that starts with the /t/ sound (e.g., top, tree, truck, turtle, tiger, tire, train, TV, twig) and then use the clay or play dough to make it.

/k/

Activity 1: Tell the children you are going to talk about things in the kitchen. Remind them that the word *kitchen* starts with the /k/ sound. Have the children name some things in the kitchen that start with the /k/ sound, such as cookies, cupcakes, cakes, carrots, cans, corn, coffee, crackers, and cocoa. For extra fun, make sugar cookies using cookie cutters and talk about the /k/ sound in *cookie* and *cutter*.

Activity 2: Cut eight strips of construction paper for each child, three inches by one inch. Give the strips of paper to the children, explaining that they will be making Curly Caterpillars. Point out that both words in Curly Caterpillar start with the /k/ sound. Show the children how to make a paper chain. Tell them to draw eyes for the caterpillar at one end of their chain.

/b/

Activity 1: Ask the children what sound the words *beanbag* and *basket* start with. Then have the children stand on a line three feet from the basket. Give the first child three beanbags. See how many baskets she can make. Have her say the /b/ sound each time she throws the beanbag.

Activity 2: Show the children a beach ball or balloon. Ask them what sound is at the beginning of these words: *beach*, *ball*, *balloon*, and *bat*. Have the children try to keep the ball or balloon in the air by batting it with their hands. Have them say /b/ each time they bat the ball or balloon.

/d/

Activity 1: Tell the children you are going to talk about dancing. The word *dancing* starts with the /d/ sound. Tell the children there are many kinds of dancing, such as square dancing, tap dancing, and rock and roll. Have the children pretend to dance. Have them say /d/ to the rhythm as they dance.

Activity 2: Tell the children you are going to talk about dinosaurs. Ask them what sound is at the beginning of the word *dinosaur*. Give them play dough and have them make their favorite dinosaur. When they are done, have them make their dinosaurs pretend to dance. Remind them that the words *dinosaur* and *dance* both start with the /d/ sound.

/g/

Activity 1: Talk about a garden and what can grow in a garden. Remind the children that the words *garden* and *grow* both start with the /g/ sound. See if they can think of some green vegetables that can grow in a garden (e.g., lettuce, cabbage, broccoli, beans, peas, asparagus). See if they can think of other green foods (e.g., grapes, limes, green apples, green bananas). Ask them what sound is in the beginning of the word *green*.

Activity 2: Tell the children you are going to talk about games. Tell them the word *game* starts with the /g/ sound. Have the children name different kinds of games they like, using a sentence like this, "My favorite game is baseball." Then have the children play one of their favorite games. It could be a card game, a board game, or a sporting game.

/ʃ/ (sh)

Activity 1: Ask the children to name some different times when they should be quiet (e.g., at the library, in a hospital, when someone is sick, or when someone is sleeping). Ask the children what they should say to tell someone to be quiet. Have them all practice politely telling each other to be quiet by saying "shhh."

Activity 2: Tell the children you are going to talk about shopping. Ask the children what sound the word *shopping* starts with. Then have the children pretend to go shopping. Have each child take a turn naming something that starts with /ʃ/ (sh) that they could go shopping for. Have them say, "I am shopping for _____." Some examples would include a shirt, shoes, sheep, shrimp, shells, sheets, and ships.

/tʃ/ (ch)

Activity 1: Tell the children that they are going to draw with chalk. Ask them what sound is at the beginning of the word *chalk*. Ask them to think of other things that start with /tʃ/ (ch) (e.g., children, cheetah, cherry, cheese, chips, chin, chicken, chimney, chair). Have each child draw a picture of a /tʃ/ (ch) word with the chalk.

Activity 2: Tell the children you are going to talk about trains. Talk about the sound a train makes when it is moving (i.e., "ch, ch, ch, ch") and when it blows its whistle loudly (i.e., "CHOO-CHOO!"). Have the children pretend to be a train, taking turns being the leader. The leader is the train engineer and can lead the train around the room and blow the whistle, saying "choo-choo." The other children should move their arms in circles as they follow the leader, pretending to be the wheels, saying "ch, ch, ch, ch." When you are done, ask the children what sound is in the word *choo-choo*.

/θ/ (th)

Activity 1: Tell the children you are going to talk about what people do when they are thirsty. Ask the children what sound the word *thirsty* starts with. Have the children take turns telling what they like to drink when they are thirsty in a sentence such as "I like to drink milk when I am thirsty." Whenever a child says a word beginning with the /θ/ (th) sound, have the children hold up their thumbs.

Activity 2: Tell the children that you are going to talk about thinking. Ask the children what sound the word *thinking* starts with. Then play a thinking game with the children. Think of a common object in the room. Have the children ask you questions to find out what you are thinking about (e.g., "Are you thinking about ____?" "No/yes, I am/not thinking about ____.").

/dʒ/ (j)

Activity 1: Talk to the children about nursery rhymes that have the /dʒ/ (j) sound in them. Point out the /dʒ/ (j) sound in the names such as *Jack* and *Jill*. Then have the children say the rhymes "Jack and Jill" and "Jack Be Nimble." Finally have the children say the rhymes again, asking them to stand up each time they say a /dʒ/ (j) sound at the beginning of a word. They'll have fun "popping" up and down.

Activity 2: Have the children name as many foods as they can that start with the /dʒ/ (j) sound (e.g., jam, jelly, Jell-O, jelly beans). Then tell the children they are going to make something that starts with the /dʒ/ (j) sound—Jell-O. Use ice cubes instead of cold water to make the Jell-O set faster. Talk about how Jell-O jiggles.

/æ/ (short a)

Activity 1: Tell the children you are going to talk about animals. The word *animal* starts with the "short a" sound. Have the children talk about different places where animals live. They live on farms, in jungles, and in zoos. Then have the children play a game of charades. Have one child pretend to be an animal and have the others try to guess what animal he or she is.

Activity 2: Tell the children that you are going to talk about astronauts. Ask them what sound the word *astronaut* starts with. Talk about things that start with /æ/ (short a) (e.g., aspirin, apple, axe, ant, ad, attic) and decide which ones an astronaut might need.

/ɛ/ (short e)

Activity 1: Talk about elephants. Remind the children that the word *elephant* starts with the /ɛ/ (short e) sound. See if they can think of a name for an elephant that starts with the /ɛ/ (short e) sound (e.g., Emily, Ed, Ellen, Elmer, Emerald, Elsie, Edna, Emma, Etta). Have them vote for their favorite names.

Activity 2: Tell the children that you are going to talk about exercises. Tell them the word *exercise* starts with the short e sound. Ask them to show you some exercises. See if they can say the "short e" sound while doing an exercise (e.g., every time they do a jumping jack).

/ɪ/ (short i)

Activity 1: Tell the children you are going to talk about measuring things. Give each child a ruler. Tell them that a ruler measures how long something is in inches. Ask the children what sound the word *inch* begins with. Tell the children there are 12 inches on a ruler. Have them measure things in the room, such as a pencil, a book, an eraser, a crayon, a stapler, a tissue box, the floor tile, and their fingers. Have them tell how long each object is in inches.

Activity 2: Tell the children you are going to talk about insects. Remind them that the word *insect* starts with the "short i" sound. Talk about insects that you see in the daytime and those you see in the evening. Ask them what sound the word *in* starts with.

/a/ (short o)

Activity 1: Tell the children you are going to talk about octopuses. Ask the children what sound the word *octopus* starts with. Tell them that "octo" means "eight" and that octopuses have eight arms or tentacles. Ask them what they would do if they had eight arms.

Activity 2: Tell the children you are going to talk about the word *on*. Ask the children what sound the word *on* starts with. Then play "Simon Says." Instruct the children to follow your directions only when you use the word *on*. If you do not say "on," they are to remain still. If a child moves when you have not said "on," he or she must sit down. Here are some examples:

Put your hands on the table.	Clap your hands.
Sit on the floor.	Touch your toes.
Stand on the carpet.	Jump up and down.
Put your hands in your pocket.	Turn around.
Put your papers on my desk.	Skip around your desk.
Put your hand on your heart.	Tap on your desk.
Write your name on the chalkboard.	Give me a pencil.

/ʌ/ (short u)

Activity 1: Tell the children you are going to talk about things that go up. Ask the children what sound the word *up* starts with. Then have them name some things that can take them up. They could go up using things like stairs, an elevator, an escalator, a ladder, or an airplane. Have each child pretend to go up using one of the items and have the group guess which one.

Activity 2: Tell the children you are going to talk about things people bake in an oven. Ask them what sound is at the beginning of the word *oven*. Have the children think of things you can bake in an oven.

/e/ (long a)

Activity 1: Tell the children you are going to talk about Abraham Lincoln. Ask the children what sound the name *Abraham* starts with. Ask if they know anything about Abraham Lincoln. Remind them that his nickname was *Honest Abe* and that *Abe* also starts with "long a." After talking about Abraham Lincoln, have the children make a top hat to wear and pretend to be the President.

Activity 2: Tell the children you are going to talk about aprons. Ask what sound the word *apron* starts with. Talk about when you might wear an apron (e.g., when you are cooking or baking). Ask the children to tell when they could wear an apron (e.g., "I could wear an apron when I bake cookies.").

/aɪ/ (long i)

Activity 1: Tell the children that you are going to talk about eyes. Tell them the word *eyes* starts with the "long i" sound. Have the children tell what they do with their eyes. Have the children stand in a line and close their eyes. Then ask them to hold the people's hands next to them. Take the first child's hand and lead the children around the room slowly. When you are done, talk about what it was like not to be able to use their eyes.

Activity 2: Tell the children you are going to talk about ice. Ask what sound the word *ice* starts with. Talk about things associated with ice (e.g., winter, snow, sledding, snowmen, skating, holidays). Have the children pretend to ice skate. Tell the children you are going to make some ice. Put water in cups and put them in the freezer. Later, have the children feel the ice and talk about what we do with ice.

/o/ (long o)

Activity 1: Tell the children you are going to sing "Old MacDonald." Tell them the word *old* starts with the "long o" sound. Explain that they will be singing about different animals that live on the farm. Have the children sing the song and stand up every time they say the O in "E-I-E-I-O."

Activity 2: Tell the children you are going to talk about oceans. Ask them what sound the word *ocean* starts with. Have the children think of things that live in the ocean. Have each child name one thing that lives in the ocean in a sentence such as "A whale lives in the ocean."

/ju/ (long u)

Activity 1: Tell the children that you are going to talk about uniforms. Ask them what sound the word *uniform* starts with. Talk about people who wear uniforms. Have the children make hats to go with different uniforms (e.g., police officer, firefighter, chef).

Activity 2: Tell the children you are going to talk about uses of tools. Talk about how the word *use* starts with the "long u" sound. Show the children some tools and ask them what they use them to do (e.g., "I use a hammer to pound nails.").

Final Sounds: Preschool—Kindergarten

◆ Once the children can identify initial sounds, begin work on final sounds. For final sounds, read stories or poems with rhymes. Point out that the last sound in the rhyming word is the same (e.g., *look/book* both end with /k/). After a while, ask the children to tell you the ending sound in the rhyme.

◆ Show the children pictures from Appendix C, pages 162-163. Ask them which two end with the same sound. The words are listed below, reading across the line:

comb	duck	book
cat	net	man
log	pig	foot
pan	tub	cab
can	dog	moon
car	fish	dish

◆ Say a word (e.g., *pen*). Tell the children that the word ends with the /n/ sound. Then tell them you will say three more words and you want them to tell you which one ends with the same sound as the word *pen* (e.g., *dog, man, fish*).

◆ Repeat the activity above but have the children pick a word that doesn't end the same as the target word.

◆ Make posters with pictures of words that end with the same sound.

◆ Play "Post Office" with final sounds in words. Tape paper mailboxes on a chart with a letter printed on the front of each mailbox. (See the sample mailbox in Appendix C, page 161. Cut a slot in the mailbox as indicated.) Give the children pictures that end with the sounds made by the letters written on the mailboxes. Have each child name his or her picture and then "mail" it into the proper mailbox by sliding it into the slot. Begin with just two mailboxes. Gradually add more mailboxes as the children learn more sounds.

◆ Sing this song to the tune of "Pop Goes the Weasel" to encourage the children to listen for final sounds.

> "What's the sound that ends these words?
> What sound is at the end?
> What's the sound that ends each word?
> Tell me what you heard."

Then say these three words: *bad, road, mad*. When someone says /d/, say "Yes. Now let's sing this verse." Be sure to make the sound, not the letter.

> "/d/ is the sound that ends these words.
> /d/ is the sound at the end.
> /d/ is the sound that ends each word.
> /d/ is what you heard."

Repeat using the following sets of words:
/d/ *bad, road, mad*
/p/ *top, cup, lap*
/b/ *tub, cab, sub*
/k/ *duck, cake, beak*
/g/ *dog, leg, mug*
/f/ *knife, safe, off*
/v/ *cave, live, wave*
/m/ *some, ham, lamb*
/n/ *can, pen, fin*
/r/ *car, far, bear*
/s/ *soap, sun, safe*
/l/ *ball, tell, pill*
/z/ *buzz, fizz, raise*
/ʃ/ (sh) *dish, cash, fish*
/tʃ/ (ch) *pitch, teach, coach*
/θ/ (th) *bath, moth, path*

Medial Sounds: Kindergarten—First Grade

◆ Show the children pictures from Appendix C, pages 164-165. Ask them which pictures have the same middle sound. The words are listed below, reading across the line:

soap	road	bat
meat	sun	feet
lip	rug	fin
rake	safe	meat
spoon	lamp	food
won	fun	sip

◆ Sing this song to the tune of "Pop Goes the Weasel" to encourage the children to identify the middle sounds in words.

> "What's in the middle of these words?
> What sound is in the middle?
> What's in the middle of each word?
> Tell me what you heard."

Then say these three words: *tame, rake, wait.* When someone says /e/ (long a), say "Yes. Now let's sing this verse." Be sure to make the sound, not the letter.

> "/e/ is the middle sound in these words.
> /e/ is the sound you heard.
> /e/ is the middle sound in each word.
> /e/ is what you heard."

Repeat using the sets of words below:

/i/ (long e) *leaf, deep, meat*
/aɪ/ (long i) *mice, light, time*
/o/ (long o) *goat, bone, comb*
/æ/ (short a) *pan, bat, tack*
/u/ (long u) *food, move, loom*
/ɪ/ (short I) *pin, sit, fin*
/a/ (short o) *dog, pot, rob*
/ɛ/ (short e) *bed, red, fed*
/ʌ/ (short u "uh") *cut, some, gun*

◆ Read books with rhymes and point out how the middle sounds are the same. Also read books with a lot of assonance (i.e., repeated vowel sounds) such as *Bringing the Rain to Kapiti Plain* by Aardema (1985); *Henny Penny* by Ziefert (1997); and *Each Peach, Pear, Plum* by Ahlberg and Ahlberg (1985).

Segmenting and Blending Activities

Children need to develop word awareness which, according to van Kleeck (1998) consists of two different skills: word consciousness, an understanding that words exist apart from their referents; and word awareness, the ability to segment sentences into component words. Children demonstrate their word consciousness when they can do the following:

◆ recognize that a "long word" does not have to be a long thing (and vice versa). For example, a "train" is a long thing but a short word; a "basketball" is a long word but not a long thing.

◆ can recognize that more than one word may name a person or thing (e.g., that *mother* can be both "Mommy" and "Ashley")

◆ make-up new or silly words

Children demonstrate their abilities to segment sentences into words when they can tell that a sentence is made of two or three words. Often syllable segmenting is easier than word segmenting because of the rhythm and because function words such as *a* and *the* are hard for young children to separate from their referents. Word segmentation is easier if you use single syllable words that do not require articles. For example, "Rob cuts" is easier to segment than "The boy cuts" since young children do not recognize the article as being separate from the noun.

Even more important than the ability to segment words in a sentence is the ability to segment syllables and sounds in words. Work should progress through the following levels:

◆ syllables

◆ subsyllables

◆ phonemes

Syllable segmentation is easier than phoneme segmentation because "each syllable has a vocalic nucleus or peak of energy. This energy peak provides an audible cue that can be used in segmentation" (Catts 1991b, p. 198). Work with syllables should progress through the following levels:

◆ compound words

◆ two-syllable words

◆ three-syllable words

Liberman, Shankweiler, Fischer, & Carter (1974) found that 50% of kindergarten children can segment words into syllables but only 17 % of them could segment words into phonemes. Segmenting activities should be paired with blending activities, progressing in the same order:

◆ blending compound words

◆ blending two-syllable words

◆ blending three-syllable words

Work on phoneme segmentation should not begin until after children can segment syllables. Work on phoneme segmentation should progress through these levels:

◆ subsyllables (i.e., intrasyllables as found in onsets and rimes)

◆ two-sound words

◆ three-sound words

Choose words that begin with continuant sounds because they are longer in duration and can be pronounced in isolation, thus making it easier for children to separate them from other sounds. After these are mastered, introduce stops, beginning with voiceless stops and progressing to voiced stops. As with syllable segmenting, pair phoneme segmenting activities with blending activities, progressing through the same sequence from intra-syllables, to two-sound words, and then three-sound words.

Provide visual, tactile, and/or movement cues whenever possible (e.g., by using puzzles, disks, blocks, markers, and/or color coding). After children can segment and blend onsets and rimes and phonemes, add graphemes to the activities. Catts (1991b), in reviewing research and intervention studies, stated that "instruction in letter name and letter-sound correspondence in addition to segmentation and blending have a greater influence on reading development than interventions involving phonological awareness or sound-letter instruction alone" (p. 199).

Sound-letter (phoneme-grapheme) correspondences may be introduced in a variety of ways, but the key is to focus on the phoneme to grapheme relationship rather than the opposite. One way to do so would be to use the stories in Appendix C, pages 130-160 to introduce the sounds and then the letters. Copy the characters and post them around the room just like letters of the alphabet. Also add any unusual spellings of the sounds to the characters as they are found. For example, if a child in the room is named Sean, add the *S* to Shirley Sheep as an alternate way to spell /ʃ/ (sh). This is particularly important for vowels as there are many ways to spell the different vowel sounds.

S = Sean

Segmenting Words in Sentences: Preschool/Kindergarten

◆ Tune children in to the words in sentences. Have them clap their hands or jump for the number of words in the sentence. Be sure to use only content words (i.e., do not include articles as children at this age level cannot separate these from the word itself). Also be sure to use only one-syllable words. Following are some examples to try:

Rob cuts paper.	Kate reads books.	Mae draws cats.
Lin drinks milk.	Jake jumps rope.	Chase eats soup.

For variety, use the pictures illustrating the previous sentences found in Appendix C, pages 166-168. Select three children. Give one a subject noun (e.g., *Rob*), one a verb (e.g., *cuts*), and one an object noun (e.g., *bread*). Have the children stand side-by-side in front of the group and point to each one as you say the words to the sentence. Next have them stand apart and ask the other children to say what word the first child has, then the second child, and then the last child. Then tell the children to stand next to each other again and have the group say the whole sentence. Be sure to point out that each child represents a different word. Point to the printed words on the picture cards to help the children begin to associate the printed words with the spoken words.

◆ Give each of three children picture cards representing each word in the sentences listed above. Have each child stand up as his or her word is called. Have them stand together as you and the other children "read" the sentence. (Be sure the children stand left to right as the children in their seats look at them so that the words are read from left to right as in a book.) Point to the words on the picture cards so the children begin to see the relationship between print and words; they will also begin to see the boundaries between the words.

◆ Using the pictures from Appendix C, pages 166-168, put the noun subjects in a pile, the verbs in a pile, and the noun objects in a pile. Let each of three children choose a picture from each of the piles. Have them stand in front of the group, holding their pictures. Have the other children "read" the sentence. Some sentences will make sense, but some will be silly. Have fun laughing at the silly sentences. Be sure to have the children move apart so you can talk about the first word, the next word, and the last word; then have them slide together and say the whole sentence.

◆ Give the children the two- and three-word sentence pictures from Appendix C, pages 169-171. For the two-word sentences, have them color the box under the first word green to indicate "start" and the last one red to indicate "stop." For the three-word sentences, color the first box green, the next one yellow, and the last one red. Have the children point to the boxes as you name the words. Have them count the words.

After they are successful at this task, say the sentences but do not let them see the pictures. Encourage them to clap for each word and tell how many words (two or three) they heard.

Syllable Segmenting: Preschool/Kindergarten

◆ Have the children clap out the syllables in their names.

◆ Tell them you are going to say someone's name in "little bits" and see if they can guess who the person is. Once they guess, repeat the name in parts and have them blend the sounds together to make a word.

◆ Talk about how words are made up of parts. Begin with compound words. Give the children a compound word and ask them to clap for each part. Then ask them to tell you the "first little part of the word" and the "last little part of the word." After they can tell you the two words, tell them to put the two words together and say the whole word. For variety, have two children stand up front; point to each child as you say each part of a compound word. Then have them move apart. Ask the other children what part of the word the first child was and then what part the second child was. Then have the children slide back together and have the other children say the whole word. Consider using the list of compound words found on page 107.

◆ Once the children can do compound words, try two- and then three-syllable words. Have them clap their hands, tap their feet, or jump for each syllable. Ask them to tell you the "first little part" and the "last little part" for two-syllable words and the first, middle, and last part for three-syllable words. After they can tell you the parts, have them put the parts together and say the whole word. Tell them that each "part" is a syllable. You might want to use the two- and three-syllable words on pages 72-73.

◆ Have a puppet hold up a picture so the children cannot see it. Have the puppet tell the children they can have the picture if they can guess what it is. Have the puppet say the name in syllables and have the children guess what it is. Tell the children to say the word "all together."

◆ Introduce a car, truck, and train (See Appendix C, pages 172-174). Talk to the children about how the car only has one part, but the truck has two parts (cab and bed), and the train has three (or more if more cars are added) parts (engine, box car, and caboose). Tell them that words are made of parts too. The parts are syllables. Put the pictures of the car, truck, and train on the board. (It might be helpful to enlarge the pictures.) Then name some pictures (or simply name some words) and have the children decide if they have one, two, or three parts (syllables) and place the pictures with the vehicle with the same number of parts. Use words from pages 72-73 or any words related to units being discussed in class.

◆ Read *Henny Penny* by Ziefert (1997) and point out the two syllables (as well as the rhymes) in the characters' names (e.g., Henny Penny and Turkey Lurkey).

◆ Be sure to point out similarities in common compound words (e.g., the days of the week: Mon*day*, Tues*day*, Wednes*day*; numbers: thir*teen*, four*teen*, fif*teen*, six*teen*, etc.).

◆ Play a guessing game. Reach in a box and feel an object. Say its name in its syllable parts and have the children guess the object.

◆ Have the children sit in a circle. Give them pictures with words with two or three syllables. Say the word in parts and have the child with the right word hold up the picture for the word you say.

Segmenting Subsyllables (Onsets and Rimes): Kindergarten—First Grade

◆ Repeat any rhyming activities from the rhyming section. Write the rhyming words on the board and show how they change just at the beginning. "I'm a Little Teapot" is a good example since all four rhyming words retain the same final spelling (e.g., *stout, spout, shout, out*). Point out any spelling changes in other rhymes. If you have hung the characters from the sound stories (See Appendix C, pages 130-160), write alternative spellings on the appropriate sound character (e.g., in "Twinkle, Twinkle Little Star" /aɪ/ [long i] is spelled with a *Y* in "sky" and with *IGH* in "high." Write *Y* and *IGH* on Ida Icicle to show the alternative spellings of /aɪ/.). To give the children a chance to print the sounds, write the rhyming part on the board and have the children take turns writing the different beginning letter in front of it.

Long Ii

y = sky
igh = light

◆ Use common word families and have the children segment the first sound from the rest of the rime. Print consonants that can occur on cards and put them on a ring. Print a word family on the board and have the children take turns selecting a consonant from the ring, placing it in front of the word family, and "reading" the resulting word. (Be careful which letters you allow the children to select to use with the word families; if you don't, you may have some undesirable results!). You might use the groupings of the most frequent rimes (word families) listed on page 78.

Segmenting Phonemes: First Grade

◆ Read the following books:

There's a Dragon in My Wagon! (Salisbury 1998)
My Nose Is a Hose! (Salisbury 1997)
A Bear Ate My Pear! (Salisbury 1998)
There's a Bug in My Mug! (Salisbury 1997)

Point out how the beginning sound changes. Ask the children to say the beginning sound and then the rest of the word.

◆ Put together and take apart two- and three-sound puzzles from Appendix C, pages 175-183. Have the children tell the "first little part" and the "last little part" for two-sound words and the first, middle, and last parts for the three-sound words. Tell them that each "little part" is a sound. The following words are pictured on pages 175-183. Begin with words with continuant sounds at the beginning, progress to those with voiceless stops, and then to words with voiced stops:

Two-sound words

Introduce:	*First*	*Second*	*Last*
	saw	toe	bee
	shoe	tie	bow
	zoo	pie	dough
	sew	key	bye

Three-sound words

Introduce:	*First*	*Second*	*Last*
	mop	pan	bed
	map	pen	bug
	sit	cup	dog
	ship	cat	gum
	feet	tape	gate
	sheep	kite	boat
	sack	coat	duck
	duck	cake	bike

The first set of three-sound words all use short vowels and common consonant spellings (except for *C* /k/ in *cat* and *cup*). The second set includes long vowels with silent *e* or vowel digraphs as well as the consonant digraph *-ck*. Alert the children to these unusual spellings. If you have displayed the sound characters from the stories in Appendix C, pages 130-160, you can add these spellings to the sound charts (e.g., *-ee* to Ebert Eel).

◆ Give each child a sheet with three squares on it. (Appendix C, page 184.) Have the children point to two or three squares as you say the sounds of the words.

◆ Give each child three blocks. Have each child point to a block each time you say a sound in a two- or three-sound word.

◆ Using the sheet of paper with three squares on it (Appendix C, page 184), have the children put a block on a square as they say each sound of the word. Then tell them to slide the blocks together and say the whole word.

◆ Read a familiar story but sound out some of the words and have the children blend the words together. For example, in *Brown Bear, Brown Bear, What Do You See?* by Martin (1983), you might say, "I see a black /k/-/æ/- /t/ looking at me. What did I see? (cat)"

◆ Read a familiar poem or rhyme and sound out the rhyming word. Have the children blend it together. For example, you might say, "Jack and Jill went up the /h/ - /I/ - /l/. What did they go up? (hill)"

◆ Sing this song to the tune to "Skip to My Lou" to work on blending sounds. Be sure to sing slowly and make the sounds for the word, not the letters.

> "What's this word: /k/ - /æ/ - /t/?
> What's this word: /k/ - /æ/ - /t/?
> What's this word: /k/ - /æ/ - /t/?
> /k/ - /æ/ - /t/ says what?

After the children say the correct word, have them join you in this verse to the same tune:

> "*Cat* is the word - /k/ - /æ/ - /t/.
> *Cat* is the word - /k/ - /æ/ - /t/.
> *Cat* is the word - /k/ - /æ/ - /t/.
> /k/ - /æ/ - /t/ is *cat*."

Repeat using other three-sound words. (See the list on page 103 for examples of good words to use.)

◆ Sing this song to the tune of "Pop Goes the Weasel" to work on counting the sounds in words. For two-sound words use these verses:

"What are the sounds you hear in *go*?
What are the sounds in *go*?
How many sounds do you hear in *go*?
What sounds have you heard?"
"/g/ is the first sound in *go*.
/o/ is sound number two.
I hear two sounds in *go*.
Go has two sounds, it's true."

For three-sound words, use these verses:
"What are the sounds you hear in *cat*?
What are the sounds in *cat*?
How many sounds are in *cat*?
What sounds have you heard?"

"/k/ is the first sound in *cat*.
/æ/ is sound number two.
/t/ is the last sound in *cat*.
Cat has three sounds, it's true."
Repeat using other three-sound words.

◆ Give the children the paper with three squares drawn on it. (See Appendix C, page 184). Have the children listen as you say a single sound or a two or three sound word. Have them place a block on a square for each sound they hear. Ask how many sounds they heard.

Remember to begin with words that have a continuant sound at the beginning and then a vowel (two-sound words) or a continuant plus a vowel and then a stop (three-sound words). Do not use words with consonant clusters in them (e.g., *spin*) or r-controlled vowels (e.g., *fir, far, her, for*). Consider using the following words:

Two sounds		*Three sounds*	
sew	shoe	soup	soap
saw	zoo	rip	zip
show	she	sip	sit
my	me	fat	fit
moo	knee	lip	lid
no	new	ship	shut
		rib	rub
		road	ride
		mop	map
		nap	knob

◆ Hold up two pictures. Tell the children you are going to name one of the pictures in little bits or parts. Tell them to put the parts together and tell you the name of the picture. Use pictures with two or three sounds. Avoid words with *r*-controlled vowels (e.g., *for, fir, far*) as children will hear the /r/ as part of the vowel.

◆ Hold up two pictures. Ask the children if they think the words have the same number of sounds. Then say the first word one sound at a time and have them hold up one finger for each sound. Count the fingers. Then say the second word and have them hold up one finger for each sound. Count the fingers. Decide if the number was the same or different. Use two- and three-sound words, having some pairs match and some differ.

··

Manipulation Activities

··

Once children can segment and blend sounds, they can increase and reinforce their phonological awareness skills by participating in sound manipulation tasks (Catts 1991b). Manipulation tasks include the following:

◆ deleting syllables and sounds in words

◆ substituting syllables and sounds in words

◆ reversing syllables and sounds in words

Work should begin with syllables and progress to phonemes. Visual, tactile, and/or movement cues will help to simplify these high-level phonological awareness tasks. These cues help to reduce the impact of the memory demands inherent in these tasks (Catts 1991b).

This section includes two activities which require the children to recognize changes or "errors" in words in familiar passages. In addition to helping the children focus on the form of the words apart from their meanings, these activities help children recognize when changes in form affect meaning. Often children who have trouble with reading will misread words and yet not be concerned that their misread word does not make sense. These activities may help children overcome this tendency. In other words, helping them recognize errors in listening tasks may help them internalize the need for "sense-making" later at a print level. Manipulation tasks are appropriate for first graders who have succeeded on the preceding segmentation and blending tasks.

Syllable Deletion: First Grade

◆ Give each child two blocks. Tell them to point to the first block as you say the first part of a compound word and the second block as you say the second part (e.g., *cow/boy*). Have them tell you what it would be if you took away the first part (e.g., "What would *cowboy* be without *cow*?").

◆ The following compound words are appropriate to use. They are grouped by similar parts where possible so that you might work on changing the different part in these groups.

snowflake	classroom	goldfish
snowman	bathroom	catfish
snowball	lunchroom	starfish
baseball	sunshine	starlight
football	sunset	airport
footprint	sunlight	airline
footstep	moonlight	airplane
bathrobe	flashlight	toothache
bathroom	birdhouse	headache
bathmat	doghouse	earache
doormat	farmhouse	earphone
doorknob	rainbow	teabag
doorstop	raincoat	teapot
skateboard	bedtime	eggshell
scoreboard	halftime	seashell
scorecard	nighttime	seafood

◆ Have the children listen to a compound word. Have them tell you what it would be if you took away the last part (e.g., "Say *cowboy* without *boy*."). Use the words listed above.

◆ Repeat the same task but with two-syllable words that are not compound words. When the children can do two syllables, introduce three-syllable words and take away the ending syllable. Consider using the words listed on pages 72-73.

◆ Hold up pictures of people doing things. Tell the children who the people are and then ask them what the word would be if you take away the *-er* (e.g., *teacher, singer, baker, trainer, pitcher, hitter, golfer, player, bowler, dancer*).

◆ Hold up action pictures. Tell the children what the people are doing and then ask them what the word would be if you took away the *-ing* (e.g., *playing, singing, dancing, driving, cooking, mowing, stirring*).

Sound Deletion—Initial: First Grade

◆ Have each of the children say his or her name and then say it again without saying the first sound. Use your name as an example: "Sally ➔ ally."

◆ Say simple one-syllable words. Ask the children to say the word without the beginning sound. At first use words in which the remaining word is a real word like the following examples:

fat ➔ at	nice ➔ ice	pink ➔ ink
man ➔ an	rice ➔ ice	witch ➔ itch
sit ➔ it	mice ➔ ice	cold ➔ old
seat ➔ eat	late ➔ ate	band ➔ and

◆ Draw three squares on the board, left to right. Say a two- or three-sound word and point to one square for each sound (e.g., "n-o" or "d-o-g"). Ask the children what would be left if you took away the first sound (e.g., Using the word *no*, remove the first square and say, "If I take away the /n/, what sound is left?"). Later you can print the letters on the squares so the children also see the associated graphemes. You can also have two or three children stand and point to each child as you say the sounds in the words. Then ask one child to squat down and ask, "What is left?" Vary which children stand and squat.

◆ Introduce words with initial clusters. Tell the children to tell you what each word would be if you took away the first sound (e.g., "What would *stop* be if we took away the /s/?"). Since clusters are more difficult, only use ones that yield real words when the initial sound is deleted. Begin with /s/ and /f/ clusters since these are continuant sounds, which are easier to hear. After the children can do these, introduce /r/ clusters. The following words can be used:

slip/lip	slap/lap	star/tar	swing/wing
flip/lip	flap/lap	flute/lute	flag/lag
trip/rip	tray/ray	play/lay	trap/rap
bride/ride	draw/raw	drink/rink	grip/rip
plate/late	drip/rip	glow/low	blow/low

Sound Deletion—Final: First Grade

◆ Draw three squares on the board. Say a three-sound word, such as *dog*. Say each sound in the word as you point to a square. Then ask the children what the word would be if you took away the last sound (e.g., "What would *dog* be if we took away the /g/?").

◆ Hold up a picture of a common object. Name it but omit the last sound. Ask the children to say the whole name and then tell you what sound was missing.

Substitution: First Grade

◆ Begin with word substitutions. Use the pictures from the word segmenting tasks in the Appendix C, pages 166-168. Put the subject noun pictures in one pile, the verbs in another pile, and the object nouns in a third pile. Give one picture from each pile to three different children. Have them stand side-by-side in the front of the class and have the rest of the class "read" the sentence. Then tell another child to pick a picture from the subject noun pile and change places with the child who has the subject noun picture. Have the children "read" the new sentence (e.g., "Rob drinks. Lin cuts."). Repeat by changing the verbs and object nouns too. Some sentences will be silly. Have the children explain what is silly (e.g., "Lin drinks cats" "Mae eats milk").

◆ Have the children create new compound words by changing the first word part. For example, take the word *house* and add different pictures in front of it to make new words, such as *birdhouse, doghouse, henhouse,* and *playhouse.* The word *ball* is also good (e.g., *baseball, football, basketball, handball, foosball*). Some of the word groups listed on page 107 will be helpful for this task too. Silly words may be suggested, and that is acceptable.

◆ Have the children create names for people by changing the first part (e.g., *teacher, singer, player*). Be sure to stress that the child is to change the first part of the word (e.g., *teach, sing, play*) to another verb to create a new word.

◆ Have the children create new actions by changing the first part of a verb (e.g., *playing, walking, kicking*). Be sure to stress that the child is to change the first part (e.g., *play*) to another verb to create a new word.

◆ Have the children produce rhymes by changing the first letter of a word family. For example, take a word family, such as *-an*. Put it on a card. Then on another card, print letters. Place the different letters in front of the word family and say the word. Emphasize that the end (rime) stays the same but the beginning (onset) changes. Remind the children that all of these words rhyme because the end sounds the same. You might color code the rime part one color (e.g., red) and then change the colors for the beginning letters/sounds (graphemes/phonemes) so that the children can see that the ending stays the same. Some examples are listed on the next page.

-at	-ake	-et
bat	cake	pet
cat	bake	bet
rat	rake	let
hat	lake	set
sat	take	vet
fat	make	pet

◆ Print a word family on the board (e.g., -at). Tell the children to copy it on their papers. Then tell each child to put a /m/ in front of it to make a new word. Have them say the new word. Repeat using one or two more sounds (e.g., /s/ and /f/).

◆ Draw three squares on the board. Say a three-sound word, such as bat. Point to each square as you say the sounds. Ask the children to change the first sound to a different one and then tell you the new word (e.g., "What would bat become if we change the /b/ to /s/?"). After the children are good at changing the initial sound, repeat the activity but change the final sound. Finally, practice changing the middle sound. For spelling practice, print the sounds in the squares. Then have a child come forward and erase the first sound (letter) and replace it with another sound (letter). Have the other children copy the new word on their papers.

◆ Have the children substitute long for short vowels in the following words. Print the words on the board so the children can see how long vowel words have a silent e at the end. Use these words as examples:

pin/pine	rat/rate	bit/bite
kit/kite	fat/fate	Sam/same
pan/pane	mat/mate	man/mane
fin/fine	Tim/time	cut/cute
cub/cube	can/cane	dim/dime

After the children understand the vowel changes, only print the short vowel word on the board and have the children take turns copying the word, adding the e, and then reading the new word.

◆ Give each child three blocks or squares, one green, one yellow, and one red. Place three squares on the board in the same colors and order (green on left, yellow in middle, and red on right). Say a three-sound word, such as fat and point to a square as you say each sound (e.g., /f/ = green, /æ/ (short a) = yellow, /t/ = red). Have the children point to their blocks and say the same sounds. Then tell them to change the green sound to /l/ and have them tell you the new word. Later, change the red sound and finally, change the yellow sound. Pair this activity with the letters so that the children see the grapheme relations. Begin with sounds that have only single graphemes. Later, add sounds that are represented by more than one grapheme, but be sure to keep these letters together in the sound square (e.g., /k/ - c; /e/ - long a; /n/ - ne). The following list shows a sequence of changes that can be made:

Finals	Initials	Medials
cat/cab	can	cone/cane
pat/pad	pan	pane/pine
mad/mat	man	mane/mine

◆ Have the children sing familiar songs and then repeat them using different sounds. For example, sing "Happy Birthday to You" but replace the beginning sound with a designated sound, such as /b/ (Bappy Birthday bo Boo), or simply use a repeated syllable throughout, such as "puh" (Papa papa pa pa) (Yopp 1992). Introduce as many different sounds as you desire. Show the printed letter, make its sound, and then join in the song. Be sure to demonstrate for the children how to change the sounds. You could also have the children change the beginning sound in lines, such as "Fe - fi - fiddley - I -O (e.g., Se - Si - Siddley -I -O) or in "Old MacDonald" (e.g., instead of E-I-E-I-O, make it Be-Bi-Be-Bi-Bo). You could have the children use the first sounds of their names to make the change (e.g., Laura would say, "LeLiLeLiLo").

Reversal: First Grade

◆ Read the following books by Slepian and Seidler. The characters in these books mix up sounds by substituting or reversing sounds in words. For example, they say "gubblebum" for bubble gum and "bellyjeans" for jelly beans.

   The Hungry Thing (2001)
   The Hungry Thing Returns (1990)

◆ Have the children listen to a compound word and then reverse the parts (e.g., *bookbag/bagbook*, *birdhouse/housebird*). Give each of the children two blocks to represent each syllable in the word (e.g., *book/bag*) and then have them reverse the blocks and say the reversed word.

◆ Repeat the same activity but with three sound words. Have the children reverse the beginning and ending sounds (e.g., *pot/top; ten/net; pat/tap; bat/tab*). Use blocks to represent each sound and then reverse them. For variation, print one word on the board (e.g., *pot*) and have the children take turns reversing the letters and then reading the new word. This activity could also be done by having the children write the new word on their own papers at their desks.

◆ Have the children reverse sounds in common word pairs (e.g., *sheet* and *pillow* = *peet* and *shillow*). Examples are listed below.

salt and pepper	heel and toe
couch and chair	knife and fork
shoes and socks	hot and cold
shirts and pants	hat and coat
cats and dogs	stop and go
coffee and tea	nickel and dime
good and bad	happy and sad
thunder and lightning	shirt and tie
land and sea	hook and ladder
tooth and nail	hammer and saw
left and right	pie and cake
boat and motor	night and day

Recognizing Word and Sound Errors: First Grade

◆ Using the pictures from Appendix C, pages 185-186, have the children decide what the mistake is and how to fix it. Tune them in to the word and sound errors.

◆ Recite a line from a familiar poem or song and change a word. Have the children tell what is wrong or different.

Reverse words (grammatical):	Jill and Jack went up the hill.
Substitute words:	Mack and Bill went up the hill.
Reverse words (ungrammatical):	Jack and Jill the hill went up
Reverse sounds in words:	Jack and Jill hent up the will.
Mix up sequences:	To get a pail of water,
	Jack and Jill went up the hill.

What materials are available for use in developing phonological awareness skills?

A number of products have been developed to target phonological awareness. Following is a list of some of the products and their targeted areas.

◆ *CLUES for Phonemic Awareness*

Authors: Diann Lapp, James Flood, Linda Lungren, and Rebecca Geiss (2000)
Publisher: Curriculum Associates, Inc.
Grade: Prekindergarten to first

A four-book series, with 14 lessons in each book, targets consonants, vowels, phonograms, common blends, digraphs, and diphthongs in activities including sound matching, sound isolation, blending, segmenting, and manipulation. Children are encouraged to "sing it, feel it, hear it, say it," and "find it."

◆ *Just for Me! Phonological Awareness*

Author: Margaret Warner (1999)
Publisher: LinguiSystems
Grade: Prekindergarten to first

Hands-on activities are provided to help students learn basic phonological awareness skills. Activities involving rhyming, syllables, compound words, and sounds are included.

◆ *The Lindamood Phoneme Sequencing Program for Reading, Spelling, and Speech* (The LiPS Program)

Authors: Patricia Lindamood and Phyllis Lindamood (1998)
Publisher: Pro-Ed
Grade: Kindergarten and up

Conscious processing of sensory information is taught to help students develop metacognitive phonemic awareness. Materials include mouth drawings, manipulatives, a videotape, and a manual.

◆ *Phonemic Awareness in Young Children: A Classroom Curriculum*

Authors: Marilyn Jager Adams, Barbara R. Foorman, Ingvar Lundberg, and Terri Beeler (1998)
Publisher: Paul H. Brookes Publishing Co.
Grade: Preschool to first

Suggestions are provided for developing a pre-literacy program. Activities include simple listening games, rhyming, syllable and phoneme awareness, and manipulation tasks. It is designed to be used for 15-minute lessons.

◆ *Phonics, Phonemic Awareness, and Word Recognition Activities*

Author: Brenda Calabretta (2000)
Publisher: Teacher Created Materials, Inc.
Grade: Kindergarten to first

Many activities for developing phonemic awareness, alphabet knowledge, phonics, structural analysis (onsets and rimes, compound words, and suffixes), sight words, and context clues are described including stories and art projects.

◆ *The Phonological Awareness Kit: Primary*

Authors: Carolyn Robertson and Wanda Salter (1995a)
Publisher: LinguiSystems
Ages: 5-8

This kit is an instructional supplement to any regular classroom reading program. It includes materials (picture cards, number cards, cubes, chips, and home activity suggestions) for developing phonological awareness skills.

◆ *Phonological Awareness Training Program*

Authors: Joseph Torgeson and Brian Bryant (1994a)
Publisher: Pro-Ed
Grade: Kindergarten to first

Activities designed to complement reading instruction for children at risk for reading problems are divided into four sets: warm-up, sound blending, sound segmenting, and reading and spelling. A manual, tape, chips, and picture/letter cards are included.

◆ *Road to the Code*

Authors: Benia Blachman, Eileen Ball, Rochella Black, and Darlene Rangel (2000)
Publisher: Paul H. Brookes Publishing Co.
Grade: Kindergarten to first

Forty-three lessons which focus on phoneme awareness are included. The "Say-It-and-Move-It" technique is used as part of each lesson. The program is designed for use with small groups (4-5) for 15-20 minutes daily for 11 weeks, although it could be modified to fit other schedules.

◆ *Silly Songs: For Phonology and Sound Awareness*

Author: Beverly Banker (1998)
Publisher: Thinking Publications
Grade: Preschool to second

Thirteen phonologically-loaded songs based on familiar melodies are provided.

◆ *Sounds Abound: Listening, Rhyming, and Reading*

Authors: Hugh Catts and Tina Olsen (1993)
Publisher: LinguiSystems
Grade: Prekindergarten to third

Activities target rhyming, beginning and ending sounds, segmenting and blending sounds, and putting sounds together in words. Lists of songs, rhymes, and books to use when targeting phonological awareness are included as well as a pre-test and post-test.

◆ *Sounds Abound: Multisensory Phonological Awareness*

Author: Jill Teachworth (2001)
Publisher: LinguiSystems
Grade: Prekindergarten to second

Phonological awareness activities plus tactile-kinesthetic cues for sounds are provided. It also includes cards for letter matching, puzzles for letters, ABC kids, and pictures for initial sounds.

◆ *The Sounds Abound Program: Teaching Phonological Awareness in the Classroom* (developed by the Stern Center for Language and Learning)

Authors: Orna Lenchner and Blanche Podhajski (1998)
Publisher: LinguiSystems
Grade: Prekindergarten to third

Pictures, songs, and familiar games to target phonological awareness in the classroom are provided. It includes a video demonstrating how to integrate these activities into the classroom.

◆ *Sounds Abound: Storybook Activities*

Author: Sandy Lachance (2002)
Publisher: LinguiSystems
Grade: Prekindergarten-second

Phonological awareness activities are incorporated into 43 stories. Activities include word awareness, syllable awareness, rhyming, initial and final sound awareness, blending of onsets and rimes plus phonemes, and manipulating activities.

◆ *Sounds Good to Me*

Author: John Bryant (1998)
Publisher: Thinking Publications
Age: 4-8 years

Themes, songs, and poetry are used to teach listening, rhyming, and syllable and sound identification.

Phonological awareness is a critical piece in learning to read—a piece that has sometimes been ignored or minimized. This book has provided a rationale for its inclusion in the critical years from preschool through first grade (and beyond for those children who have not developed phonological awareness skills) as well as suggestions for assessment and development of phonological awareness skills. As noted throughout, though, phonological awareness is not the only factor involved in the development of literacy during these years.

What factors affect literacy development?

Emergent Literacy Skills

What are emergent literacy skills?

Emergent literacy skills are "skills, knowledge, and attitudes that are the developmental precursors to reading and spelling" (American Speech-Language-Hearing Association [ASHA] 2001a, p. 4). Emergent literacy skills include early phonological awareness skills (including letter knowledge and phoneme-grapheme correspondences) as well as the following:

◆ print awareness

◆ print motivation

◆ print experience

To develop literacy skills, children must develop an awareness of print function, print conventions, and print forms. They must interact with adults in fun reading and writing activities and be surrounded by literacy-rich environments at home and at school. They must learn how to hold a book and to associate letters with words and how to use writing tools to produce letters. They must also have opportunities to experience and participate in literacy events involving reading and writing.

How can we help children develop emergent literacy skills?

As speech-language pathologists, reading specialists, learning disabilities teachers, and classroom teachers, we need to help young children do the following:

◆ Recognize literacy artifacts by pointing out print in the environment (e.g., on blocks, posters, T-shirts, and cereal boxes)

◆ Learn literacy conventions by showing them how to hold a book and turn the pages and by showing them how to hold and use a pencil or crayon to make marks, letters, and numbers

◆ Engage in literacy events by providing opportunities for joint book reading and joint writing (e.g., giving them a crayon to write pretend letters or lists with while we do the same)

◆ Learn literacy terminology by talking about books, covers, words, letters, authors, and titles

◆ Recognize the importance of print by filling our rooms with literacy artifacts and activities and by pointing out literacy events whenever possible

◆ Explore literacy through many channels (e.g., through songs, books, videos, and computers) as well as tactile experiences (e.g., by feeling letters made with clay)

We also need to provide families with the knowledge and materials needed to increase home literacy experiences. Workshops and hand-outs are good ways to start, but we can also encourage families to participate in book fairs and library programs. Establishing cooperative programs with local and state agencies as well as with service organizations are additional ways to secure funding to purchase books and other literacy materials for families.

Normal language skills

What normal language skills must be acquired?

Normal language skills were described in Chapter 2, pages 12-34. As indicated throughout this book, reading and spelling are part of language. They have their roots in oral language development. Normal early oral language development is needed for reading and spelling to develop. Strong reading and spelling skills are needed for oral language to continue to develop and grow. Young children need to develop normal phonologic, semantic, syntactic, morphologic, pragmatic, and textlinguistic skills. They also need to develop metalinguistic abilities.

How can we help children develop normal language skills?

We can work together to provide language-rich environments in which opportunities to develop vocabulary and basic concepts, syntactic, morphologic, pragmatic, and narrative skills are common. "Children need to experience reading, spelling, and writing for authentic communication purposes in which vocabulary, grammar, and discourse skills converge" (ASHA 2001a, p. 16). Additionally, we need to provide explicit instruction in phonological awareness.

While many young children will develop phonological awareness naturally within a language-rich environment, some will not. Therefore, systematic phonological awareness training needs to be incorporated into preschool, kindergarten, and first grade curricula. Phonological awareness training must progress through normal developmental sequences targeting awareness of rhyming, syllables, phonemes, and sound-symbol (phoneme-grapheme) associations through activities involving categorization, segmentation and blending, and manipulation. To be effective, it must be combined "with explicit knowledge of the alphabetic principle and its application to decoding and spelling words" (ASHA 2001a, p. 15).

We also need to work together to identify those at risk for reading and spelling disabilities so that early intervention can be provided.

Who is at risk?

According to the American Speech-Language-Hearing Association (2001a), children with limited literacy experiences, lack of print awareness, and/or language deficits are particularly at risk for reading and spelling disabilities, ". . . especially when accompanied by the following:

◆ Family history of speech and language development or literacy problems

◆ Difficulties in phonological processing, including phonological awareness

◆ Multiple articulation problems and/or reduced speech intelligibility

◆ Word-finding difficulties, including delays in rapid automatic naming

◆ Language comprehension problems

◆ Discrepancy between auditory-language comprehension and spoken-language expression

◆ Immature syntactic and semantic development

◆ Delayed narrative discourse abilities

◆ Verbal memory difficulties" (ASHA 2001a, p. 7).

As professionals we need to identify at-risk children early, refer them for appropriate testing, and, when indicated, see that direct intervention services are provided.

Millions of children will develop reading and spelling disabilities that will have devastating effects on their academic and social development. Many will have phonological awareness deficits at the root of, or at least as a significant part of, their reading and spelling disabilities. The period for the normal development of phonological awareness skills is short—from preschool (3-4 years) through first grade (6-7 years). Development of phonological awareness skills can be enhanced with appropriate and explicit training during these years. Phonological awareness training may also be beneficial for children beyond these grades who have not yet developed phonological awareness skills. Hopefully, *The Source for Phonological Awareness* has provided you with the rationale, motivation, and knowledge needed to provide phonological awareness training.

Appendix A
Early Identification of Language-based Reading Disabilities: A Checklist[1]

Child's Name: _____ Birthday: _____

Date Completed: _____ Age: _____

This checklist is designed to identify children who are at risk for language-based reading disabilities. It is intended for use with children at the end of kindergarten or beginning of first grade. Each of the descriptors listed below should be carefully considered and those that characterize the child's behavior/ history should be checked. A child receiving a large number of checks should be referred for a more in-depth evaluation.

Speech Sound Awareness

❑ doesn't understand and enjoy rhymes
❑ doesn't easily recognize that words may begin with the same sound
❑ has difficulty counting the syllables in spoken words
❑ has problem clapping hands or tapping feet in rhythm with songs and/or rhymes
❑ demonstrates problems learning sound-letter correspondences

Word Retrieval

❑ has difficulty retrieving a specific word (e.g., calls a sheep a "goat" or says "you know, a woolly animal")
❑ shows poor memory for classmates' names
❑ speech is hesitant, filled with pauses or vocalizations (e.g., "um," "you know")
❑ frequently uses words lacking specificity (e.g., "stuff," "thing," "what you call it")
❑ has a problem remembering/retrieving verbal sequences (e.g., days of the week, alphabet)

Verbal Memory

❑ has difficulty remembering instructions or directions
❑ shows problems learning names of people or places
❑ has difficulty remembering the words to songs or poems
❑ has problems learning a second language

Speech Production/Perception

❑ has problems saying common words with difficult sound patterns (e.g., animal, cinnamon, specific)
❑ mishears and subsequently mispronounces words or names
❑ confuses a similar sounding word with another word (e.g., saying "The Entire State Building is in New York")
❑ combines sound patterns of similar words (e.g., saying "escavator" for escalator)
❑ shows frequent slips of the tongue (e.g., saying "brue blush" for blue brush)
❑ has difficulty with tongue twisters (e.g., she sells seashells)

Comprehension

☐ only responds to part of a multiple element request or instruction
☐ requests multiple repetitions of instructions/directions with little improvement in comprehension
☐ relies too much on context to understand what is said
☐ has difficulty understanding questions
☐ fails to understand age-appropriate stories
☐ has difficulty making inferences, predicting outcomes, drawing conclusions
☐ lacks understanding of spatial terms such as left-right, front-back

Expressive Language

☐ talks in short sentences
☐ makes errors in grammar (e.g., "he goed to the store" or "me want that")
☐ lacks variety in vocabulary (e.g., uses "good" to mean happy, kind, polite)
☐ has difficulty giving directions or explanations (e.g., may show multiple revisions or dead ends)
☐ relates stories or events in a disorganized or incomplete manner
☐ may have much to say, but provides little specific detail
☐ has difficulty with the rules of conversation, such as turn taking, staying on topic, indicating when he/she does not understand

Other Important Factors

☐ has a prior history of problems in language comprehension and/or production
☐ has a family history of spoken or written language problems
☐ has limited exposure to literacy in the home
☐ lacks interest in books and shared reading activities
☐ does not engage readily in pretend play

Comments:

[1]This checklist was prepared by Hugh W. Catts, University of Kansas. Some descriptors have been taken from *Language for Learning: A Checklist for Language Difficulties*, Melbourne, Australia: OZ Child.

Catts, H.W. (1997). The early identification of language-based reading disabilities. *Language, Speech, and Hearing Services in Schools*. 28, 86-89. © American Speech-Language-Hearing Association. Reprinted with permission.

Appendix B

Examples of Clinician-designed Tasks for Screening Early Literacy

Target	Task
Written language awareness	1. The child is presented with a series of tasks during a shared book reading activity to assess his or her knowledge of print and book reading conventions (e.g., print directionality, functions of book elements [cover page, title, etc.]). For example, the child is instructed to "show me the front of the book," "show me just one word," or "show me where I begin to read" (Clay, 1979; Justice & Ezell, 2000). 2. The child is asked to read words that are common to his or her environment (e.g., logos, labels, signs); words are presented in a continuum from highly contextualized to decontextualized (Gillam & Johnston, 1985). 3. The child is asked to differentiate printed depictions of various written language units, including *word, letter, number,* and *sentence* (Lomax & McGee, 1987).
Phonological awareness	1. The child is asked to detect one word from a set of three words that differs on the basis of a common phoneme or rhyme. For example, the child is asked to identify the odd word from the set *fish/dish/book* (rhyme detection) or *bed/hair/bell* (alliteration detection) (Maclean, Bryant, & Bradley, 1987). 2. The child is asked to produce words starting with a target phoneme or rhyming with a target word. For example, the child is asked to "tell me a word that starts with /m/" or "tell me a word that rhymes with hat" (Chaney, 1992). 3. The child is asked to delete a sound from a target word. For example, the child is asked to say "*bat* without the /b/" (Lonigan, Burgess, Anthony, & Barker, 1998). 4. The child is asked to "break a word apart" into its component pieces. For example, the child is asked to say all the parts of the words *go* or *ride* (Yopp. 1988). 5. The child is asked to identify the number of phonemes in a target word. For example, the child is asked to tap out the number of sounds contained in the word *bat* (Liberman, Shankweiler, Fischer, & Carter, 1974).
Letter name knowledge	1. The child is presented with a series of upper- or lowercase letters and is asked to say the name of each letter (expressive task) or to point to a letter as its name is spoken by an examiner (receptive task) (Justice & Ezell, 2000). 2. The child is asked to recite the alphabet (Felton, 1992). 3. The child is presented with a chart of all of the alphabet letters and is asked to name the letters as fast as he or she can (this task measures rapid letter naming ability; Blachman, 1984).
Grapheme-phoneme	1. The child is shown an alphabet letter and is asked to produce the correspondence sound that "goes with the letter," or is provided a sound and is asked to name the letter that "goes with the sound" (Juel, 1988).
Literacy motivation	1. The child is shown pictures of literacy events (e.g., a child reading) and is asked to indicate if this is a happy or sad event by pointing to a smiling or frowning face (Frijters, Barron, & Brunello, 2000). 2. The child is engaged in a variety of literacy tasks (e.g., book reading, writing) and his or her level of engagement is described from a continuum from no or low engagement to high engagement (Kaderavek & Sulzby, 1998).
Home literacy	1. Parents are administered a checklist or questionnaire regarding home literacy materials and activities to determine the child's access to and participation in such events (Allen &—Mason, 1989; Dickinson & DeTemple, 1998). 2. A home visit is conducted by which to ascertain the frequency and nature of home literacy opportunities (e.g., Dickinson & Tabors, 1991).

Justice, L.M., Invernizzi, M.A., & Meier, J.D. (2002). Designing and implementing an early literacy screening protocol: Suggestions for the speech-language pathologist. *Language-Speech-Hearing Services in Schools.* 33. 84-101. © American Speech-Language-Hearing Association. Reprinted with permission.

Appendix C
Royal Puppets

Color the figures of Queen Alpha and King Bets and their twin children, Princess Tammy and Prince Sammy. Cut out each figure and glue it on a tongue depressor to make a puppet. Use the puppets with the activity on page 77.

Rhyming and Non-rhyming Picture Pairs

Cut out the pairs of pictures below and use them with the activity on page 77. You will need to color (or have the children color) the square red.

cat	hat	cat	dog
car	jar	car	truck
bed	red	bed	chair
house	mouse	house	garage

Rhyming and Non-rhyming Picture Pairs

Cut out the pairs of pictures below and use them with the activity on page 77. You may want to color (or have the children color) the lime green.

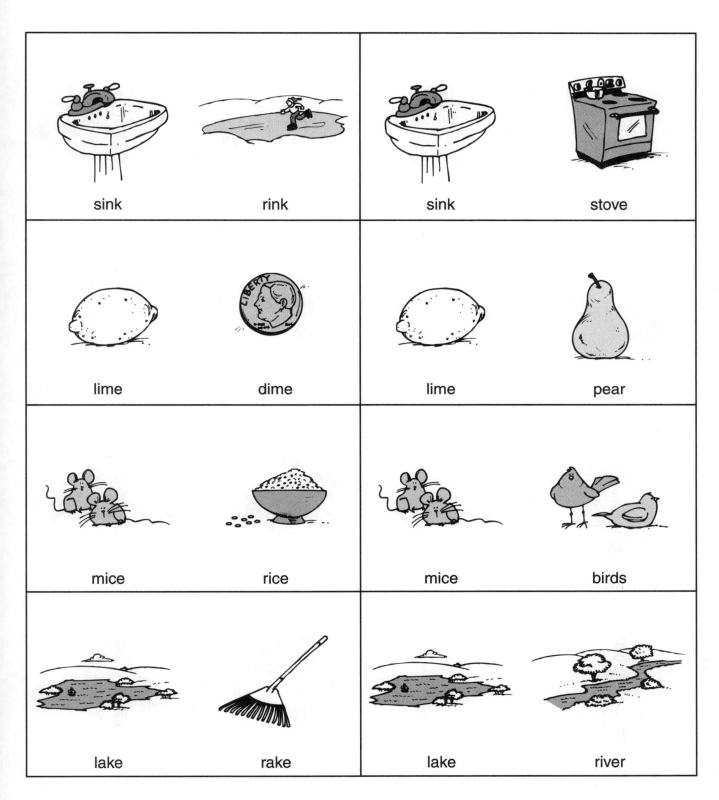

sink	rink	sink	stove
lime	dime	lime	pear
mice	rice	mice	birds
lake	rake	lake	river

125

Short Vowel Rhyming Pictures

Cut out the pictures and use them with the activity on page 78.

Short Vowel Rhyming Pictures

Cut out the pictures and use them with the activity on page 78.

Beginning Sound Pictures

Cut out the picture strips and use them with the activity on page 81.

Beginning Sound Pictures

Cut out the picture strips and use them with the activity on page 81.

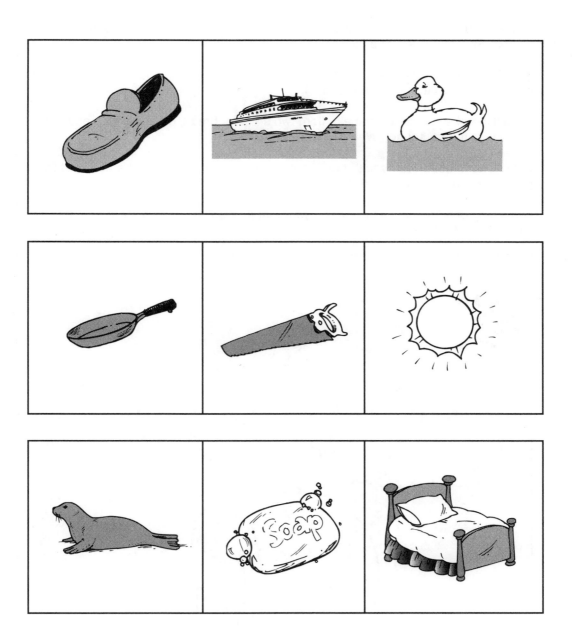

Silly Sally

Read this story to the children. Post the story somewhere in the classroom. Talk about the sound the letter makes. If you wish, copy the story and send it home for practice. Have the children tell the story to someone at home.

Silly Sally was such a silly girl. She was always asking her friends Sam and Sue to solve riddles. Help Sam and Sue solve these riddles.

"I'm thinking of something you wear on your eyes when it's sunny outside. It starts with the /s/ sound. What is it?" (sunglasses)

"I'm thinking of something you make from two slices of bread, peanut butter, and jelly. It starts with the /s/ sound. What is it?" (sandwich)

"I'm thinking of something you put on a horse's back so you can ride the horse. It starts with the /s/ sound. What is it?" (saddle)

"I'm thinking of something you wear on your foot that isn't a shoe. It starts with the /s/ sound. What is it?" (sock)

I know what sound Silly Sally's name starts with! Ask me and I'll tell you.

Fay Fox

Read this story to the children. Post the story somewhere in the classroom. Talk about the sound the letter makes. If you wish, copy the story and send it home for practice. Have the children tell the story to someone at home.

"Oh, I can't wait. I can't wait!" said Fay Fox. "I'm going to go to Florida today. I'm going to hunt for worms tonight and then go fishing. I'm going to play football and, of course, I have to eat. Let's see. I hope I packed everything." Fay looked around her. She saw her fishing pole, her flashlight, her football, and her food. Did Fay Fox remember to bring everything she needed so she can hunt for worms, fish, play football, and eat?

I know what sound Fay Fox's name starts with! Ask me and I'll tell you.

Harvey Hound

Read this story to the children. Post the story somewhere in the classroom. Talk about the sound the letter makes. If you wish, copy the story and send it home for practice. Have the children tell the story to someone at home.

Harvey Hound was digging a hole. Beside him were a hammer, a hatchet, a handkerchief, and a hat. When he had a hill of dirt beside him, he said, "I'm so happy. Now I have a special hiding place for my treasures." He put the hammer, the hatchet, and the handkerchief in the hole. There was no room for the hat. What do you think Harvey Hound should do with the hat?

I know what sound Harvey Hound's name starts with! Ask me and I'll tell you.

Molly Moose

Read this story to the children. Post the story somewhere in the classroom. Talk about the sound the letter makes. If you wish, copy the story and send it home for practice. Have the children tell the story to someone at home.

Molly Moose had just received some money from her mom. "What should I buy?" she asked. "I need some more marbles and I need a mask for my costume. Maybe I should buy some more mittens or go see that Mars movie." How do you think Molly Moose should spend her money?

I know what sound Molly Moose's name starts with! Ask me and I'll tell you.

N n   Nurse Nora

Read this story to the children. Post the story somewhere in the classroom. Talk about the sound the letter makes. If you wish, copy the story and send it home for practice. Have the children tell the story to someone at home.

Ned hurt his nose. The doctor wanted Nurse Nora to take care of Ned last night, so she did. When she got home, Nurse Nora was tired. She took a nap. When she woke up, Nurse Nora had to decide what to do. She could knit, read the newspaper, or help her friend Nancy nail pictures on the wall. She could even look for her fishing net. What do you think Nurse Nora should do first? What should she do next?

I know what sound Nurse Nora's name starts with! Ask me and I'll tell you.

Vera Vet

Read this story to the children. Post the story somewhere in the classroom. Talk about the sound the letter makes. If you wish, copy the story and send it home for practice. Have the children tell the story to someone at home.

Vera Vet loved animals. She had four favorites: Vince, Val, Vicky, and Victor. Every night after work, she drove Vince, Val, Vicky, and Victor to the park in her van. At the park, they liked to watch people play volleyball. Sometimes, Vera Vet shared her vanilla ice-cream cone with her friends. What kind of animals do you think Vince, Val, Vicky, and Victor are?

I know what sound Vera Vet's name starts with! Ask me and I'll tell you.

Zippy Zookeeper

Read this story to the children. Post the story somewhere in the classroom. Talk about the sound the letter makes. If you wish, copy the story and send it home for practice. Have the children tell the story to someone at home.

Zippy Zookeeper loved the zoo. All day long, Zippy took care of the zoo animals. Sometimes Zippy fed the zoo animals. Sometimes Zippy washed the zoo animals. Sometimes Zippy even talked to the visitors about the zoo animals. If you were a zookeeper, what would you tell the visitors about the zoo?

I know what sound Zippy Zookeeper's name starts with! Ask me and I'll tell you.

Wally Window Washer

Read this story to the children. Post the story somewhere in the classroom. Talk about the sound the letter makes. If you wish, copy the story and send it home for practice. Have the children tell the story to someone at home.

Wally Window Washer loved to wash windows. He liked to use window washer fluid to wash car windows. One day, when he was washing the window, he winked at a wiggling baby. Why do you think the baby was wiggling? Next, he saw a child wading in a puddle. Why do you think the child was wading in the puddle? Wally always washed his windows on Wednesday. Why do you think Wally washed windows on Wednesday?

I know what sound Wally Window Washer's name starts with! Ask me and I'll tell you.

Yolanda Yawner

Read this story to the children. Post the story somewhere in the classroom. Talk about the sound the letter makes. If you wish, copy the story and send it home for practice. Have the children tell the story to someone at home.

Yolanda Yawner always yawned. She yawned when she played with her yo-yo. She yawned when she knitted with yarn. She even yawned when she played in her yard. She yawned and yawned and yawned again! Why do you think Yolanda yawned so much?

I know what sound Yolanda Yawner's name starts with! Ask me and I'll tell you.

Luther Lizard

Read this story to the children. Post the story somewhere in the classroom. Talk about the sound the letter makes. If you wish, copy the story and send it home for practice. Have the children tell the story to someone at home.

Luther Lizard was a lazy lizard. All he did was sit in the sunlight, looking around. Then one day he heard a roar. "Maybe that's a leopard or even a lion!" thought Luther Lizard. "I'd better hide!" Moving one leg at a time, he moved slowly toward a log. Near the log, he saw a lollipop, some lettuce, and some lemonade. "I sure am hungry!" he thought. Do you think Luther Lizard stopped to eat lunch? Why?

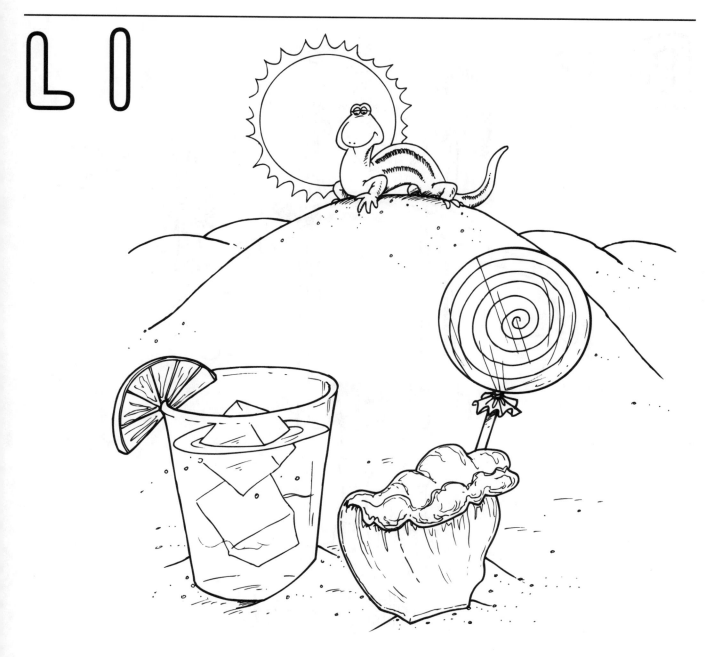

I know what sound Luther Lizard's name starts with! Ask me and I'll tell you.

Ruthie Robot

Read this story to the children. Post the story somewhere in the classroom. Talk about the sound the letter makes. If you wish, copy the story and send it home for practice. Have the children tell the story to someone at home.

Today was the day of the race. Ruthie Robot was so excited! She just knew she'd get a ribbon this year. Just before the race, she ate some raisins. Soon it was time to begin. Ruthie ran like a rocket. She ran past Rick and Rhoda and Richard. She ran past Rudy and finally, Ralph. She reached the finish line before anyone else. "Thank you," she said when she got her blue ribbon. Why did Ruthie Robot get a blue ribbon?

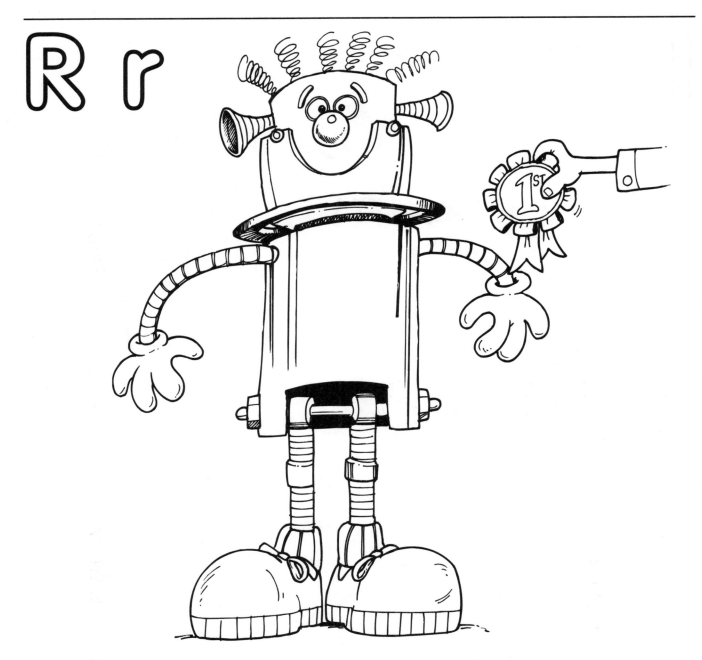

I know what sound Ruthie Robot's name starts with! Ask me and I'll tell you.

Polly Penguin

Read this story to the children. Post the story somewhere in the classroom. Talk about the sound the letter makes. If you wish, copy the story and send it home for practice. Have the children tell the story to someone at home.

"Where's my pencil?" said Polly Penguin. "I'll bet it's in your purse or in your pocket," said her friend Pig. "It's not there," said Polly Penguin. "Maybe I lost it by the pond, by the pole, or by the pool." Where do you think Polly Penguin will find her pencil?

I know what sound Polly Penguin's name starts with! Ask me and I'll tell you.

Talented Tim

Read this story to the children. Post the story somewhere in the classroom. Talk about the sound the letter makes. If you wish, copy the story and send it home for practice. Have the children tell the story to someone at home.

Talented Tim was a tiger. He was a very exciting tiger. He could balance three teapots on his nose! He could juggle ten tennis balls! Talented Tim could even balance a table on his tongue. One day his teacher said, "Class, we're going to have a talent show next week. I want everyone to be in the show." What do you think Talented Tim should do for the talent show?

I know what sound Talented Tim's name starts with! Ask me and I'll tell you.

Kathy Kitten

Read this story to the children. Post the story somewhere in the classroom. Talk about the sound the letter makes. If you wish, copy the story and send it home for practice. Have the children tell the story to someone at home.

Kathy Kitten was so tired. She was at a ranch and had just roped her first calf. "That's hard work," she said to herself. Kathy Kitten went to her cabin for a nap. When she woke up, she thought, "Now I could explore the cave, canoe down the river, or look for the keys to my car." What do you think Kathy Kitten should do first?

K k

I know what sound Kathy Kitten's name starts with! Ask me and I'll tell you.

Billy Baboon

Read this story to the children. Post the story somewhere in the classroom. Talk about the sound the letter makes. If you wish, copy the story and send it home for practice. Have the children tell the story to someone at home.

Billy Baboon woke up and stretched. "What a busy day I'm going to have today," he said. "I have to blow up my new balloon. I have to bake some cookies for Aunt Betty. And I have to buy some new boots. Then I'll be able to go to the beach. Well, I'd better get out of bed," he thought. He got up, got dressed, and then thought about what he would do first. What do you think Billy Baboon decided to do first?

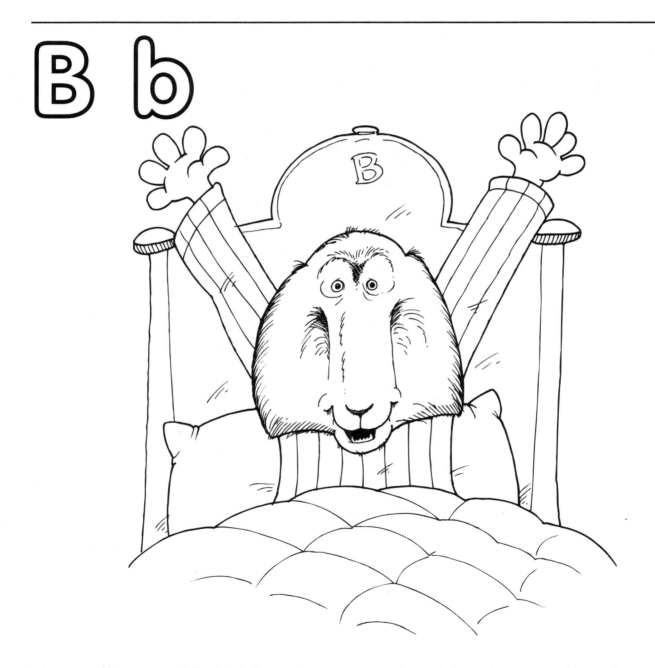

I know what sound Billy Baboon's name starts with! Ask me and I'll tell you.

Dolly Donkey

Read this story to the children. Post the story somewhere in the classroom. Talk about the sound the letter makes. If you wish, copy the story and send it home for practice. Have the children tell the story to someone at home.

Dolly Donkey was visiting her cousins, Dan and Donna. She had so much fun! First Dolly Donkey danced with Dan and Donna. Then they dug in the sand, played with a dump truck, and drew pictures of dolls, dogs, ducks, and deer. Dolly Donkey even helped Dan look up some words in the dictionary. What do you think Dolly enjoyed doing the most?

I know what sound Dolly Donkey's name starts with! Ask me and I'll tell you.

Gary Goose

Read this story to the children. Post the story somewhere in the classroom. Talk about the sound the letter makes. If you wish, copy the story and send it home for practice. Have the children tell the story to someone at home.

Gary Goose said to his friend Gail. "Let's go out to the garden. There are two ghosts out there. I just know it! They're wearing goofy goggles and they're chewing gum. I'll bet if we listen carefully, we'll even hear their guitar music." "Oh, that's silly," said Gail. "I don't think we're going to see any ghosts." Do you think Gary and Gail will see any ghosts in the garden? Why?

I know what sound Gary Goose's name starts with! Ask me and I'll tell you.

Shirley Sheep

Read this story to the children. Post the story somewhere in the classroom. Talk about the sound the letter makes. If you wish, copy the story and send it home for practice. Have the children tell the story to someone at home.

Shirley Sheep loved to go shopping. One day, while she was at a clothing store, she bought lots of things that started with the /sh/ sound. See if you can figure out what Shirley Sheep bought.

You wear this on the bottom part of your body when it's hot outside. It covers your bottom and part of your legs. Sometimes it has a zipper. What is it? (shorts)

You wear these on your feet, but they aren't socks. What are they? (shoes)

You wear this on the top part of your body. It covers your shoulders, stomach, and back. Sometimes it buttons up the front. What is it? (shirt)

SH sh

I know what sound Shirley Sheep's name starts with! Ask me and I'll tell you.

Theodore Thinker

Read this story to the children. Post the story somewhere in the classroom. Talk about the sound the letter makes. If you wish, copy the story and send it home for practice. Have the children tell the story to someone at home.

Theodore Thinker was thinking. Last Thursday, his friends Thelma and Shawn gave him a surprise birthday party for his thirteenth birthday. "I'd sure like to do something special for them," he thought. "I could let them use my new thermos or my thread. Or I could let them use my new thermometer or my thumbtacks. What do you think Theodore decided to do?

TH th

I know what sound Theodore Thinker's name starts with! Ask me and I'll tell you.

Cherry Cheetah

Read this story to the children. Post the story somewhere in the classroom. Talk about the sound the letter makes. If you wish, copy the story and send it home for practice. Have the children tell the story to someone at home.

Cherry Cheetah got a charm bracelet for her birthday. She had never had one before. "Let's see," she thought. "The next time I go to the store, I'll have to buy some charms to put on the chain." Cherry Cheetah sat in her chair and made a list of things to buy. "I'm going to buy another chair, some chalk, a gold cherry, some cheese, and a little gold chicken." Which things are for Cherry's charm bracelet?

I know what sound Cherry Cheetah's name starts with! Ask me and I'll tell you.

Jerry Joker

Read this story to the children. Post the story somewhere in the classroom. Talk about the sound the letter makes. If you wish, copy the story and send it home for practice. Have the children tell the story to someone at home.

Jerry Joker put on his jeans and his jacket. He jumped into his jeep and headed to Jack's house. Jerry was going to help Jack draw some jungle animals for the zoo newspaper. After greeting Jack, Jerry said, "You draw the giraffe, the cow, and the lion. I'll draw the monkey, the tiger, and the gerbil." Jerry Joker likes to play jokes on people. Do you think all these animals belong in the jungle? Which ones don't belong?

I know what sound Jerry Joker's name starts with! Ask me and I'll tell you.

Adam Actor

Read this story to the children. Post the story somewhere in the classroom. Talk about the sound the letter makes. If you wish, copy the story and send it home for practice. Have the children tell the story to someone at home.

Adam Actor needed a break from acting. He decided to have an afternoon snack, but he couldn't decide what to eat. After thinking and thinking, he decided to eat an apple. He was still hungry, so he decided to eat some animal crackers, but there were only three of them left. "I'm still hungry!" he said. What do you think Adam Actor should eat next?

Short Aa

I know what sound Adam Actor's name starts with! Ask me and I'll tell you.

Eddie Egg

Read this story to the children. Post the story somewhere in the classroom. Talk about the sound the letter makes. If you wish, copy the story and send it home for practice. Have the children tell the story to someone at home.

Eddie Egg wanted to be an engineer. He just couldn't decide what kind of engineer he wanted to be. Should he be the engineer on a train? Then he could drive trains. Should he be an electrical engineer? Then he could work with computers and electricity. Should he be a civil engineer? Then he could design buildings and bridges. Eddie Egg just couldn't decide. What kind of engineer do you think Eddie Egg should be?

Short Ee

I know what sound Eddie Egg's name starts with! Ask me and I'll tell you.

Icky Iguana

Read this story to the children. Post the story somewhere in the classroom. Talk about the sound the letter makes. If you wish, copy the story and send it home for practice. Have the children tell the story to someone at home.

Icky Iguana itched! Oh, how he itched! Every inch of him itched! "Why do I itch? Oh, why, oh why, oh why?" asked Icky. "My ears itch and my head itches. Even my tummy itches! Maybe it's because of something I ate last night. Or it could be because I got a mosquito bite. Maybe it's because I need to take a bath!" Why do you think Icky Iguana itched?

Short Ii

I know what sound Icky Iguana's name starts with! Ask me and I'll tell you.

Ozzie Otter

Read this story to the children. Post the story somewhere in the classroom. Talk about the sound the letter makes. If you wish, copy the story and send it home for practice. Have the children tell the story to someone at home.

Ozzie Otter was having a delightful time climbing on rocks and diving into the water. First he climbed on the big rock. Then he climbed on the little one. Back and forth Ozzie Otter went, climbing and diving, climbing and diving. Ozzie Otter was having a lot of fun! Do you ever climb on things? What do you climb on?

Short Oo

I know what sound Ozzie Otter's name starts with! Ask me and I'll tell you.

Uppidy Up

Read this story to the children. Post the story somewhere in the classroom. Talk about the sound the letter makes. If you wish, copy the story and send it home for practice. Have the children tell the story to someone at home.

Uppidy Up liked to go up. He went up in elevators. He went up escalators. Uppidy even went up in hot air balloons, airplanes, and helicopters. One rainy day, while Uppidy was walking under his umbrella, the wind took Uppidy Up for a long ride. He thought that was fun! Would you like to go up? What would you like to go up in?

Short Uu

I know what sound Uppidy Up's name starts with! Ask me and I'll tell you.

Ada Ape

Read this story to the children. Post the story somewhere in the classroom. Talk about the sound the letter makes. If you wish, copy the story and send it home for practice. Have the children tell the story to someone at home.

It was Ada Ape's birthday. She was eight years old. What an exciting day! Her cake would have eight candles. Eight children were coming to her party. She would probably get eight presents. What would be a good present for Ada Ape now that she's eight?

Long Aa

I know what sound Ada Ape's name starts with! Ask me and I'll tell you.

Ebert Eel

Read this story to the children. Post the story somewhere in the classroom. Talk about the sound the letter makes. If you wish, copy the story and send it home for practice. Have the children tell the story to someone at home.

Ebert Eel was growing up. Last year he had trouble tying his shoe, zipping his coat, and writing his name. Now while tying his shoe, Ebert Eel thought, "This is easy!" While zipping his coat, Ebert Eel thought, "This is easy!" And while writing his name, Ebert thought, "This is easy too!" Ebert Eel was growing up. What do you find easy to do now that you're getting bigger?

Long Ee

I know what sound Ebert Eel's name starts with! Ask me and I'll tell you.

Ida Icicle

Read this story to the children. Post the story somewhere in the classroom. Talk about the sound the letter makes. If you wish, copy the story and send it home for practice. Have the children tell the story to someone at home.

Ida Icicle was made of ice. She had to stay cold. If she didn't, she would melt! One day Ida was going to a party. "I'm going to wear my new dress," said Ida. When she took her dress out of the closet, she saw that it was wrinkled. "Oh my," thought Ida. "I should iron my dress, but if I do, I might melt!" What do you think Ida Icicle should do?

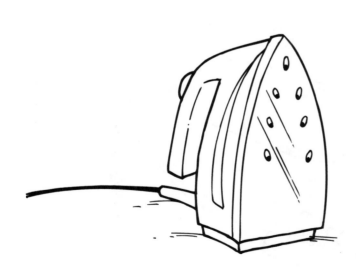

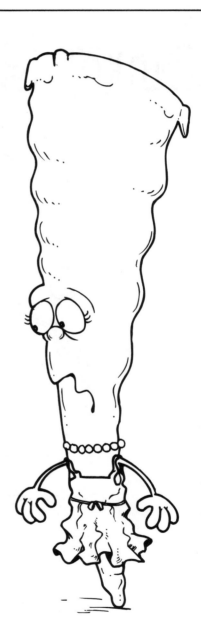

I know what sound Ida Icicle's name starts with! Ask me and I'll tell you.

Opie Oboe

Read this story to the children. Post the story somewhere in the classroom. Talk about the sound the letter makes. If you wish, copy the story and send it home for practice. Have the children tell the story to someone at home.

Opie Oboe put on his overalls, ate his oatmeal, and went to the park. Today was a special day. Opie Oboe was in a race. He was going to jump over hurdles. Opie bent down. A man yelled, "Go!" Opie jumped over the first hurdle. He jumped over the second hurdle. Finally he jumped over the third hurdle. Opie crossed the finish line. He was so excited. Opie Oboe had jumped over three hurdles! Sometimes when you run, you jump over things. What do you like to jump over?

Long Oo

I know what sound Opie Oboe's name starts with! Ask me and I'll tell you.

Ukulele User

Read this story to the children. Post the story somewhere in the classroom. Talk about the sound the letter makes. If you wish, copy the story and send it home for practice. Have the children tell the story to someone at home.

Everybody at Unicorn University liked Ukulele User. She always said nice things about other people. "You look cute!" Ukulele User said to Roberta. "Cindy, you can jump very high!" said Ukulele. "You play the ukulele very well!" she said to Donald. What nice things could you say to other people?

Long Uu

I know what sound Ukulele User's name starts with! Ask me and I'll tell you.

Mailbox Pattern

Cut out the mailbox below. Cut along the dotted line to make a slot for the "mail." Glue the mailbox on a sheet of construction paper or poster board making sure to glue only around the edges. Print the letter for the sound you are targeting on the box as illustrated. Make as many mailboxes as you need.

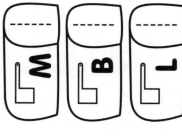

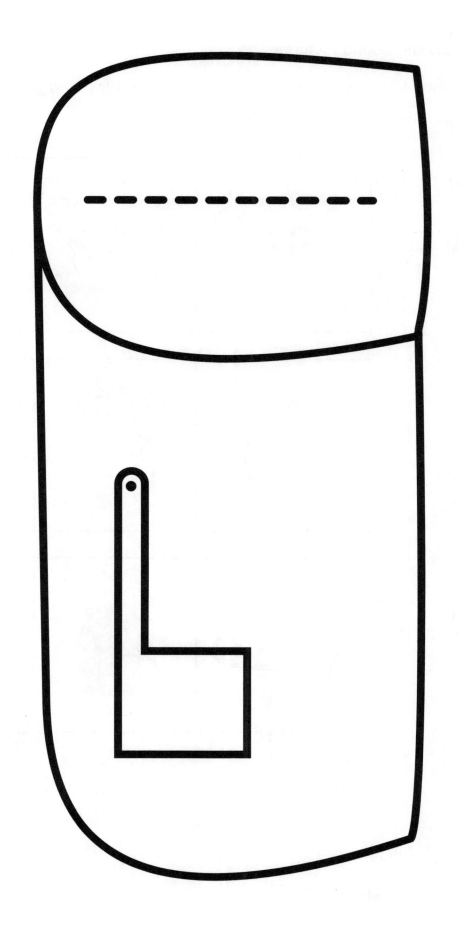

Ending Sound Pictures

Cut out the paper strips and use them with the activity on page 95.

Ending Sound Pictures

Cut out the paper strips and use them with the activity on page 95.

Middle Sound Pictures

Cut out the picture strips and use them with the activity on page 96.

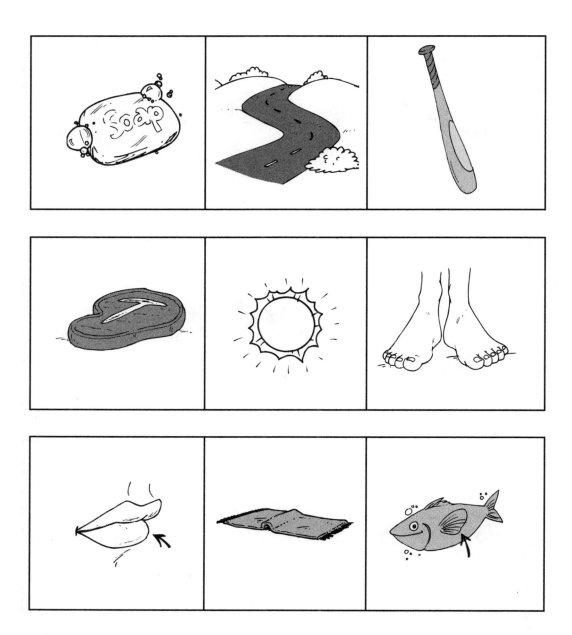

Middle Sound Pictures

Cut out the picture strips and use them with the activity on page 96.

Word Segmentation: Noun Subject Pictures

Cut out these pictures and use them to create sentences for the activities on pages 99-100.

Rob

Lin

Kate

Jake

Mae

Chase

Word Segmentation: Verb Pictures

Cut out these pictures and use them to create sentences for the activities on pages 99-100.

Word Segmentation: Noun Object Pictures

Cut out these pictures and use them to create sentences for the activities on pages 99-100.

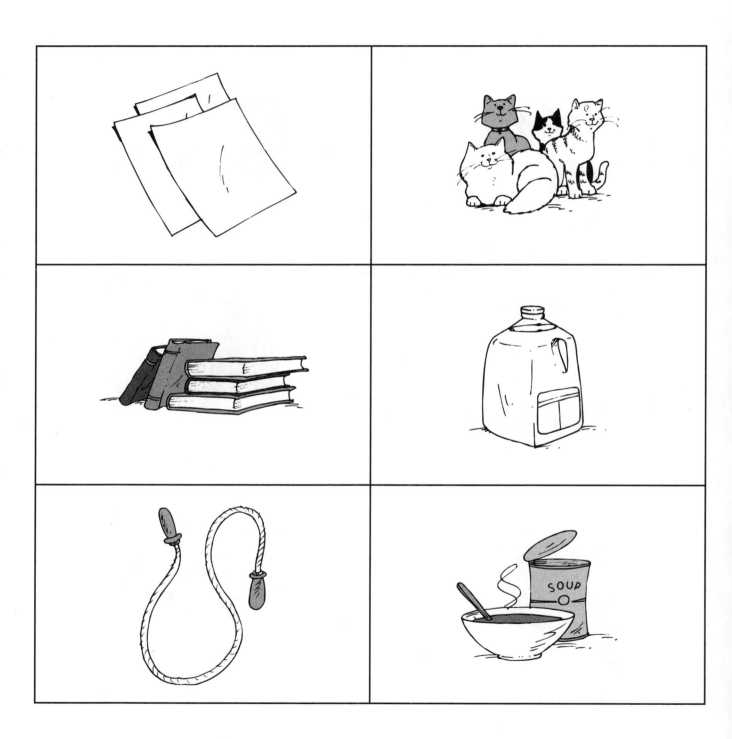

Word Segmentation: Two-Word Sentences

Cut out the pictures and give them to the children. Have them color the first circle green and the second circle red. Then have the children tell you the first and last part of the sentences. Use with activity on page 100.

Rob   **cuts.**

Lin   **drinks.**

Word Segmentation: Two-Word Sentences

Cut out the pictures and give them to the children. Have them color the first circle green and the second circle red. Have the children tell you the first and last part of the sentences. Use with activity on page 100.

Kate   **reads.**

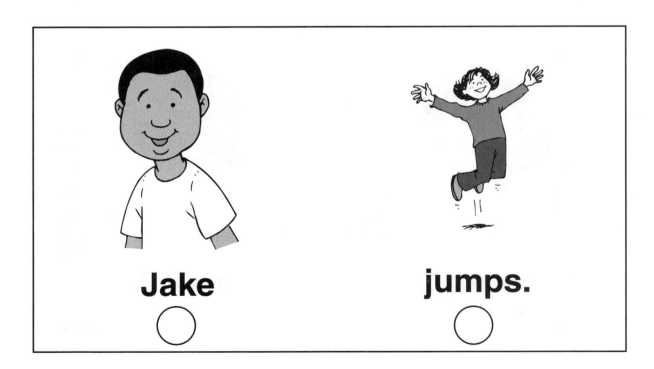

Jake   **jumps.**

Word Segmentation: Three-Word Sentences

Cut out the pictures and give them to the children. Have them color the first circle green, the middle one yellow, and the last one red. Have the children tell you the first, middle, and last part of the sentences. Use with activity on page 100.

Lin   **drinks**   **milk.**

Mae   **draws**   **cats.**

Chase   **eats**   **soup.**

Syllable Segmentation: Car

Cut out the car and use it with the syllable segmentation activities from page 101.

Syllable Segmentation: Truck

Cut out the truck parts and use them with the two-syllable segmentation activities from page 101.

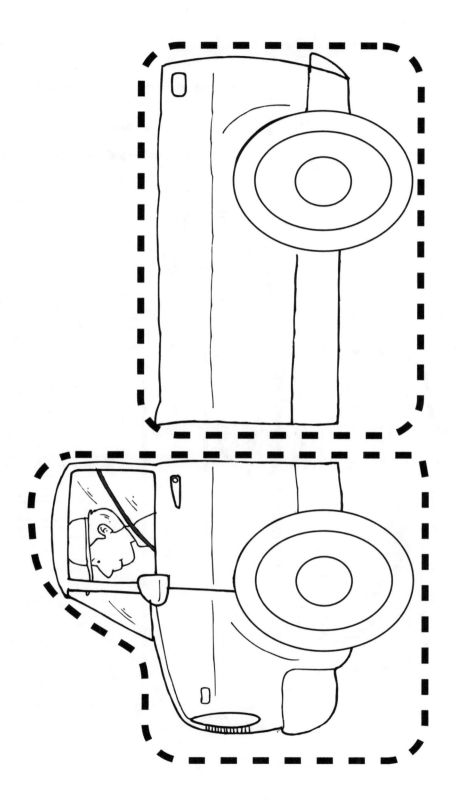

Syllable Segmentation: Train

Cut out the train parts and use them with the three-syllable segmentation activities from page 101.

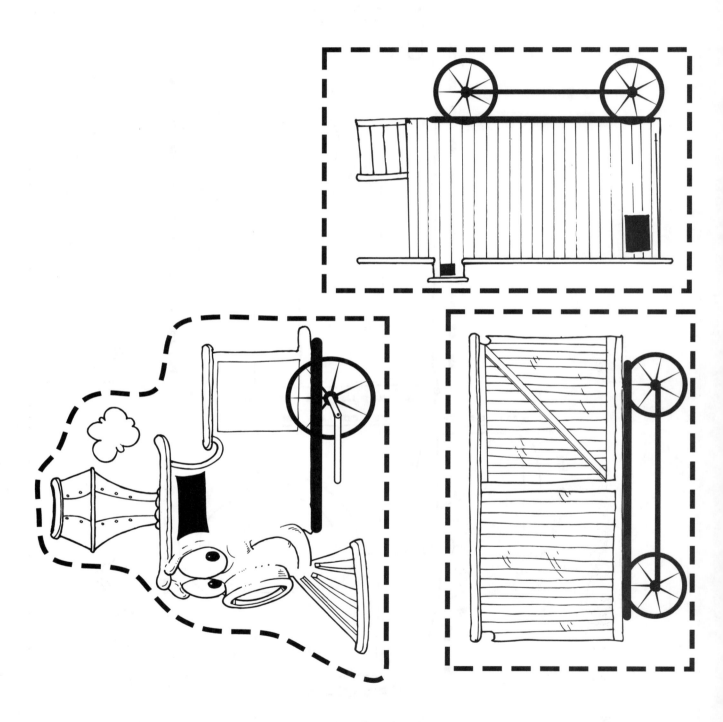

Sound Segmentation Puzzles: Two-Sound Words

Cut the pictures apart and make puzzles by cutting on the dotted lines. Use the puzzles with the sound segmentation activities on page 103. Have the children take the puzzle pieces apart and put them together. Talk about the first and last little parts of the words.

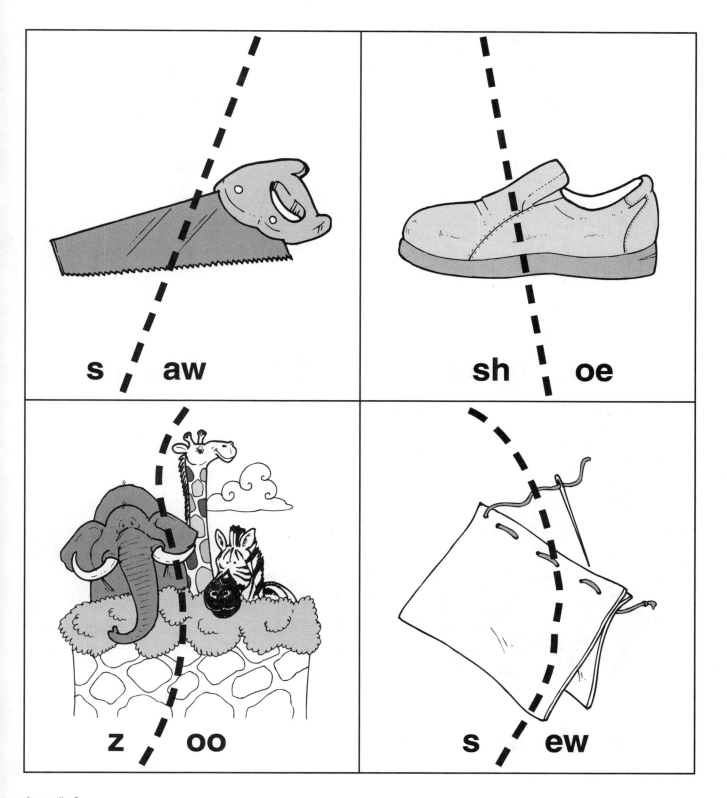

s aw

sh oe

z oo

s ew

Sound Segmentation Puzzles: Two-Sound Words

Cut the pictures apart and make puzzles by cutting on the dotted lines. Use the puzzles with the sound segmentation activities on page 103. Have the children take the puzzle pieces apart and put them together. Talk about the first and last little parts of the words.

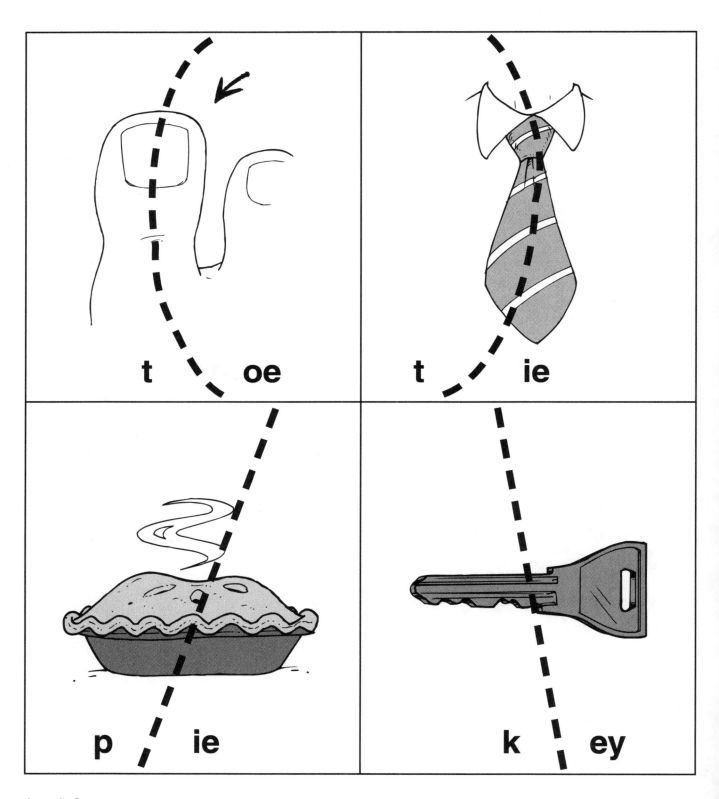

Sound Segmentation Puzzles: Two-Sound Words

Cut the pictures apart and make puzzles by cutting on the dotted lines. Use the puzzles with the sound segmentation activities on page 103. Have the children take the puzzle pieces apart and put them together. Talk about the first and last little parts of the words.

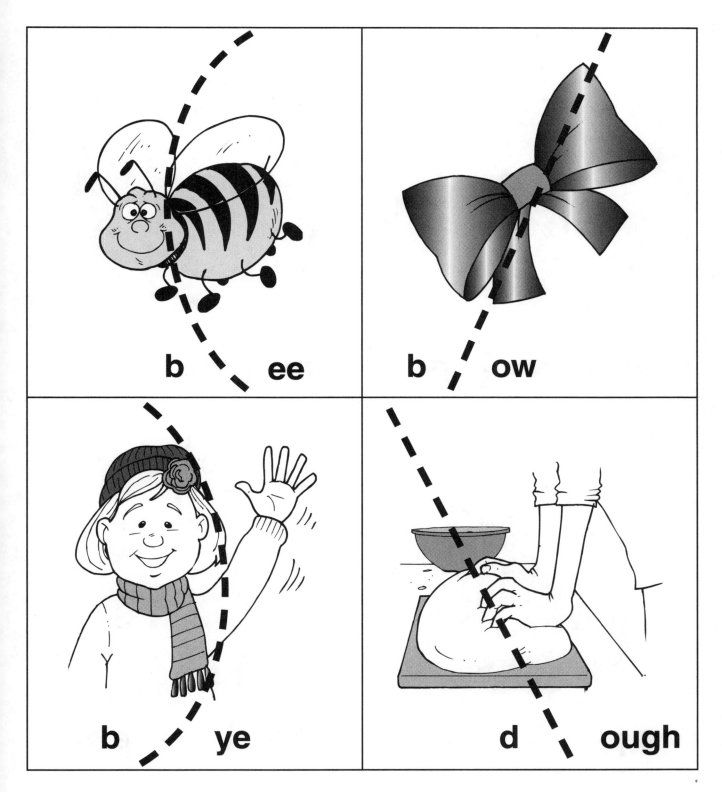

Sound Segmentation Puzzles: Three-Sound Words

Cut the pictures apart and make puzzles by cutting on the dotted lines. Use the puzzles with the sound segmentation activities on page 103. Have the children take the puzzle pieces apart and put them together. Talk about the first, middle, and last little parts of the words.

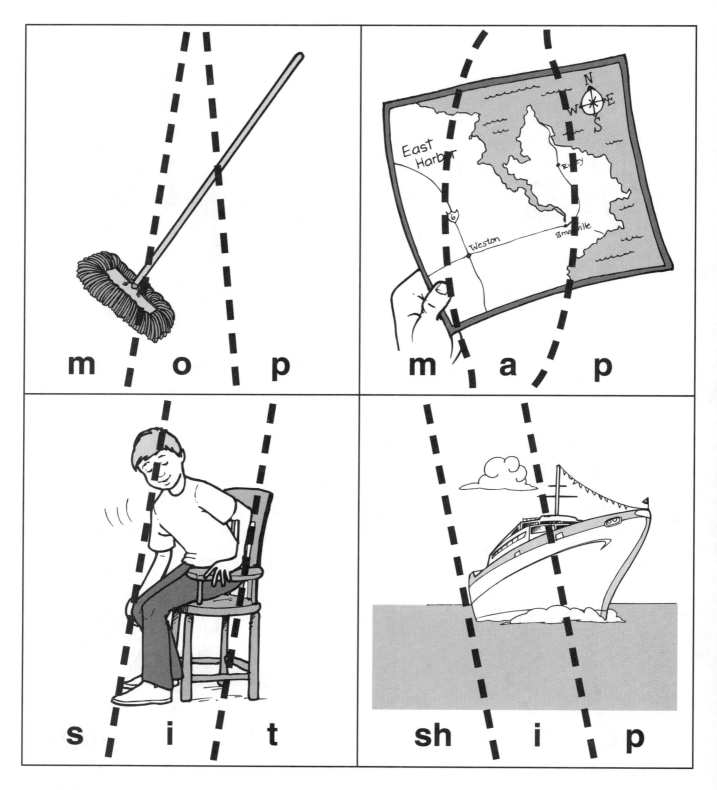

Sound Segmentation Puzzles: Three-Sound Words

Cut the pictures apart and make puzzles by cutting on the dotted lines. Use the puzzles with the sound segmentation activities on page 103. Have the children take the puzzle pieces apart and put them together. Talk about the first, middle, and last little parts of the words.

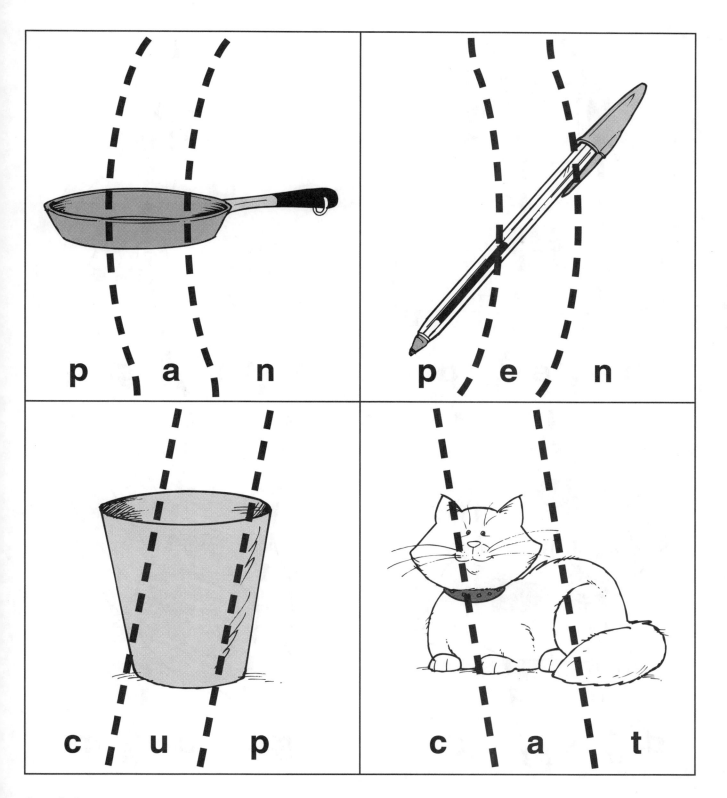

Sound Segmentation Puzzles: Three-Sound Words

Cut the pictures apart and make puzzles by cutting on the dotted lines. Use the puzzles with the sound segmentation activities on page 103. Have the children take the puzzle pieces apart and put them together. Talk about the first, middle, and last little parts of the words.

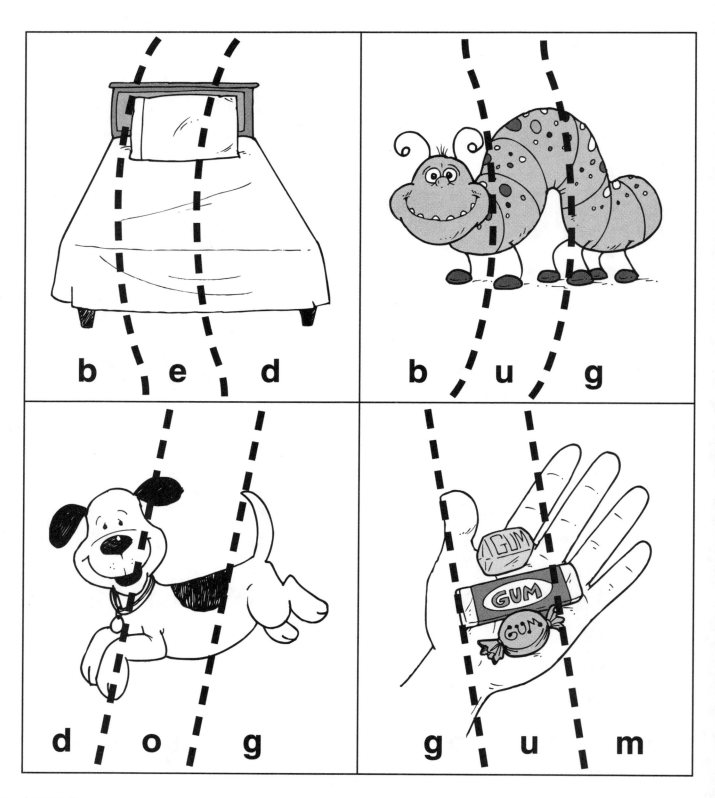

Sound Segmentation Puzzles: Three-Sound Words

Cut the pictures apart and make puzzles by cutting on the dotted lines. Use the puzzles with the sound segmentation activities on page 103. Have the children take the puzzle pieces apart and put them together. Talk about the first, middle, and last little parts of the words.

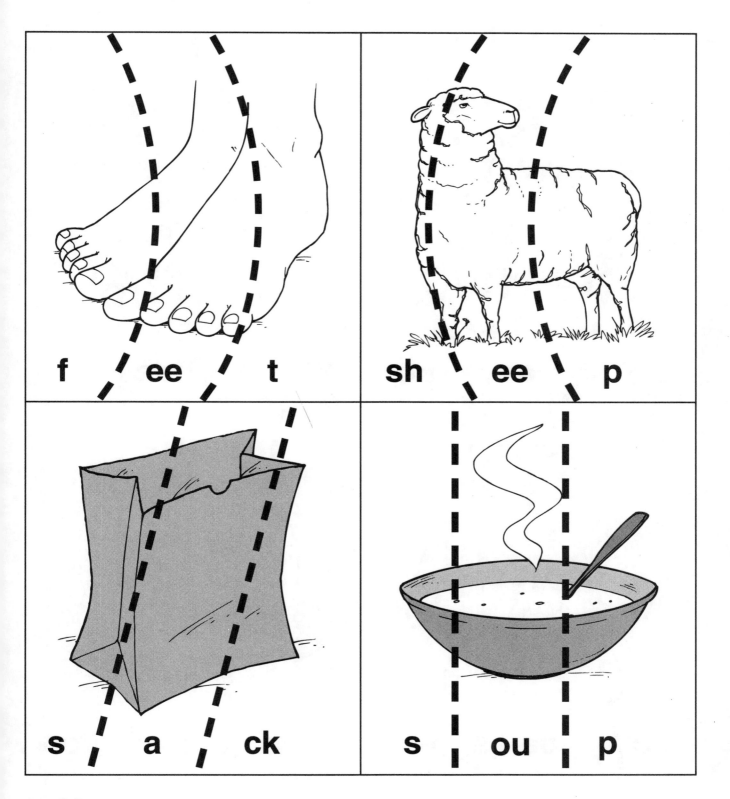

f   ee   t

sh   ee   p

s   a   ck

s   ou   p

Sound Segmentation Puzzles: Three-Sound Words

Cut the pictures apart and make puzzles by cutting on the dotted lines. Use the puzzles with the sound segmentation activities on page 103. Have the children take the puzzle pieces apart and put them together. Talk about the first, middle, and last little parts of the words.

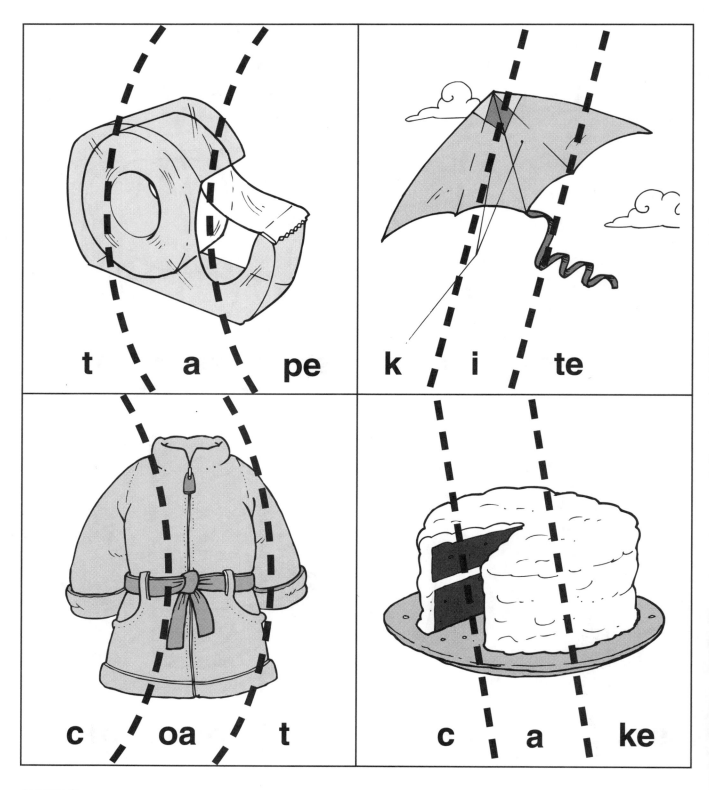

Sound Segmentation Puzzles: Three-Sound Words

Cut the pictures apart and make puzzles by cutting on the dotted lines. Use the puzzles with the sound segmentation activities on page 103. Have the children take the puzzle pieces apart and put them together. Talk about the first, middle, and last little parts of the words.

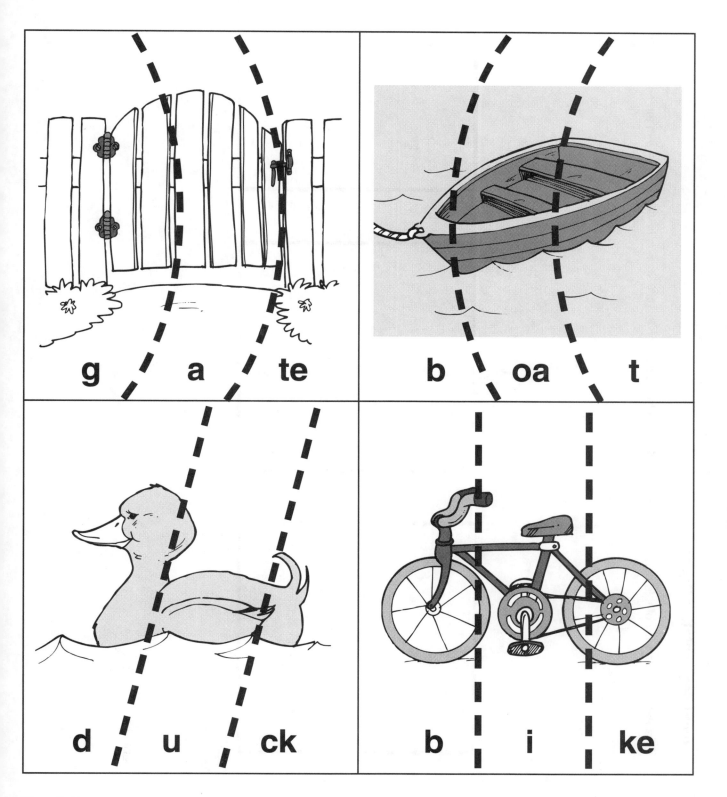

g   a   te

b   oa   t

d   u   ck

b   i   ke

Sound Segmentation Squares

Give each child a copy of this page. Use it with blocks to help the children identify sounds in words. Use with the activities on pages 104-105.

Error Identification

Give each child a copy of this page. Have the children listen to the stories as you read them. Then have the children identify the words with the sound errors. Next have the children say the words using the correct sounds. Use with the activity on page 112.

"Come on Mason," said Caitlin. "It's time to go. Put on your choat and zat." Uh-oh. Caitlin made a mistake. Can you help her?

"I'm going for a ride on my snike," said Julie. Uh-oh, Julie made a mistake. Can you help her?

"I like to drink wilk and eat tookies," said Jessie. Uh-oh. What should Jessie have said?

"Look," said CJ, "I bought a new lar." Uh-oh. What did CJ say wrong?

Error Identification

Give each child a copy of this page. Have the children listen to the stories as you read them. Then have the children identify the words with the sound errors. Next have the children say the words using the correct sounds. Use with the activity on page 112.

"I need to cut the paper. Please hand me some bissors," said Sara. Uh-oh. What should Sara have said?

The librarian said, "Put your dooks on the table." Uh-oh. What did the librarian say wrong?

Keisha said, "I have a reanut butter and melly sandwich in my lunch." Uh-oh. What did Keisha say wrong?"

Rosa said, "I need a droon to eat my ice cream." Uh-oh. What should Rosa have said?

Aardema, V. (1983). *Bringing the rain to Kapiti Plain.* Putnam, NJ: Penguin.

Adams, M. (1990). *Beginning to read: Thinking and learning about print.* Cambridge, MA: MIT Press.

Adams, M. J., & Bruck, M. (1995). Resolving the 'great debate.' *American Educator, 19*(2), 7, 10-20.

Adams, M. J., Foorman, B. R., Lundberg, I., & Beeler, T. (1998). *Phonemic awareness in young children: A classroom curriculum.* Baltimore, MD: Paul. H. Brookes Publishing Co.

Ahlberg, J, & Ahlberg, A. (1985). *Each peach, pear, plum.* New York: Viking Kestrel.

Alexander, A. W., Andersen, H. G., Heilman, P. C., Voeller, K. K., & Torgesen J. K. (1991). Phonological awareness training and remediation of analytic decoding deficits in a group of severe dyslexics. *Annals of Dyslexia, 41,* 193-206.

American Speech-Language-Hearing Association. (1995). *ASHA desk reference speech-language pathology,* III-155. Rockville, MD: American Speech-Language-Hearing Association.

American Speech-Language-Hearing Association. (2001a). Roles and responsibilities of speech-language pathologists with respect to reading and writing in children and adolescents [guidelines]. Rockville, MD: Author.

American Speech-Language-Hearing Association. (2001b). Roles and responsibilities of speech-language pathologists with respect to reading and writing in children and adolescents [position statement, executive summary of guidelines, technical report]. *ASHA Supplement 21,* 17-27. Rockville, MD: Author.

Anderson, J. Flynn. (2001). *The predictive reading profile.* East Moline, IL: LinguiSystems.

Apel, K. (2002). Serving students with spoken and written language challenges: It's in the cards. *ASHA Leader, 7*(1), 6-7.

Aram, D. M., Ekelman, B. L., & Nation, J. E. (1984). Preschoolers with language disorders: 10 years later. *Journal of Speech and Hearing Research, 27,* 232-244.

Badian, N. A. (1994). Preschool prediction: Orthographic and phonological skills, and reading. *Annals of Dyslexia, 44,* 3-25.

Baddeley, A. (1986). Working memory, reading, and dyslexia. In E. Hjelmquist & L. Nilsson (Eds.), *Communication and handicap: Aspects of psychological compensation and technical aids* (pp. 141-152). North Holland: Elsevier.

Banker, B. (1998). *Silly songs: For phonology and sound awareness*. Eau Claire, WI: Thinking Publications.

Bankson, N. W. & Bernthal, J. E. (1999). *Bankson-Bernthal test of phonology*. San Antonio, TX: The Psychological Corporation.

Bayer, J. (1984). *My name is Alice*. New York: Dial Books for Young Children.

Beck, I. L., & Juel, C. (1995). The role of decoding in learning to read. *American Educator, 19*, 8-42.

Berninger, V. W. (2000). Development of language by hand and its connections with language by ear, mouth, and eye. *Topics in Language Disorders*, 20(4), 65-84.

Bird, J., Bishop, D. V., & Freeman, N. H. (1995). Phonological awareness and literacy development in children with expressive phonological impairments. *Journal of Speech and Hearing Research, 38*, 446-462.

Bishop, D. V., & Adams, C. (1990). A prospective study of the relationship between specific language impairment, phonological disorders and reading retardation. *Journal of Child Psychology and Psychiatry and Allied Disciplines, 3*(7), 1027-1050.

Blachman, B. A. (1984). Relationship of rapid naming ability and language analysis skills to kindergarten and first-grade reading achievement. *Journal of Educational Psychology, 76*(4), 610-622.

Blachman, B., Ball, E., Black, R., & Rangel, D. (2000). *Road to the code*. Baltimore, MD: Paul H. Brookes Publishing Co.

Bradley, L., & Bryant, P. E. (1983). Categorizing sounds and learning to read–a causal connection. *Nature, 301*(3), 419-421.

Bradley, L., & Bryant, P. (1985). *Rhyme and reason in reading and spelling*. Ann Arbor: University of Michigan Press.

Bryant, J. (1998). *Sounds good to me*. Eau Claire, WI: Thinking Publications.

Bryant, P. E., Bradley, L., Maclean, M., & Crossland, J. (1989). Nursery rhymes, phonological skills, and reading. *Journal of Child Language, 16*(2), 407-428.

Burns, M. S., Griffin, P., & Snow, C. E. (Eds.). (1999). *Starting out right: A guide to promoting children's reading success*. Washington, D.C.: National Academy Press.

Calabretta, B. (2000). *Phonics, phonemic awareness, and word recognition activities*. Westminster, CA: Teacher Created Materials, Inc.

California Department of Education. (1996). *Teaching reading: A balanced comprehensive approach to teaching reading in prekindergarten through grade three.* Sacramento, CA: California Department of Education.

Catts, H. W. (1989). Speech production deficits in developmental dyslexia. *Journal of Speech and Hearing Disorders, 54,* 422-428.

Catts, H. W. (1991a). Early identification of reading disabilities. *Topics in Language Disorders, 12* (1), 1-16.

Catts, H. W. (1991b). Facilitating phonological awareness: Role of speech-language pathologists. *Language, Speech, and Hearing Services in Schools, 22,* 196-203.

Catts, H. W. (1993). The relationship between speech-language impairments and reading disabilities. *Journal of Speech and Hearing Research, 36,* 948-958.

Catts, H. W. (1996). Defining dyslexia as a developmental language disorder: An expanded view. *Topics in Language Disorders, 16*(2), 14-29.

Catts, H. W. (1997). The early identification of language-based reading disabilities. *Language, Speech, and Hearing Services in Schools, 28,* 86-89.

Catts, H. W., Fey, M. E., Zhang, X., & Tomblin, J. B. (1999). Language basis of reading and reading disabilities: Evidence from a longitudinal investigation. *Scientific Studies of Reading, 3*(4), 331-361.

Catts, H. W., Fey, M. E., Zhang, X., & Tomblin, J. B. (2001). Estimating the risk of future reading difficulties in kindergarten children: A research-based model and its clinical implementation. *Language, Speech, and Hearing Services in Schools, 32,* 38-50.

Catts, H. W., & Kamhi, A. G. (1986). Toward an understanding of developmental language and reading disorders. *Journal of Speech and Hearing Disorders, 51,* 337-347.

Catts, H. W., & Kamhi, A. G. (1999a). Defining reading disabilities. In H. W. Catts & A. G. Kamhi (Eds.), *Language and reading disabilities* (pp. 50-72). Boston: Allyn & Bacon.

Catts, H. & Kamhi, A. G. (1999b). Causes of reading disabilities. In H. W. Catts & A. G. Kamhi (Eds.), *Language and reading disabilities* (pp. 95-127). Boston: Allyn & Bacon.

Catts, H., & Olson, T. (1993). *Sounds abound: Listening, rhyming, and reading.* East Moline, IL: LinguiSystems.

Chafouleas, S. M., Lewandowski, L. J., Smith, C. R., & Blachman, B. A. (1997). Phonological awareness skills in children: Examining performance across tasks and ages. *Journal of Psychoeducational Assessment, 15*, 334-347.

Clarke-Klein, S. M. (1991). *A phonological analysis of children's spelling errors.* Unpublished doctoral dissertation, Wichita State University, Wichita, Kansas.

Clarke-Klein, S. M. (1994). Expressive phonological deficiencies: Impact on spelling development. *Topics in Language Disorders*, *14*(2), 40-55.

Cohen, R. L., & Netley, C. (1981). Short-term memory deficits in reading disabled children, in the absence of opportunity for rehearsal strategies. *Intelligence, 5*, 69-76.

Donahue, M. (1984). Learning disabled children's comprehension and production of syntactic devices for marking given versus new information. *Applied Psycholinguistics, 5*, 101-116.

Ehlert, L. (1989). *Eating the alphabet: Fruits and vegetables from a to z.* San Diego, CA: Harcourt Brace Jovanovich.

Ehri, L. C. (1997). Learning to read and learning to spell are one and the same, almost. In C. A. Perfetti, L. Rieben, & M. Fayol (Eds.), *Learning to spell: Research, theory, and practice across languages* (pp. 237-269). Mahwah, NJ: Lawrence Erlbaum Associates.

Ehri, L. C. (1998). Grapheme-phoneme knowledge is essential for learning to read words in English. In J. Metsala & L. Ehri (Eds.), *Word recognition in beginning literacy* (pp. 3-40). Hillsdale, NJ: Lawrence Erlbaum Associates.

Ehri, L. C. (2000). Learning to read and learning to spell: Two sides of a coin. *Topics in Language Disorders, 20*(3), 19-36.

Ellis, N. (1997). Interactions in the development of reading and spelling: Stages, strategies, and exchange of knowledge. In C. A. Perfetti, L. Rieben, and M. Fayol (Eds.), *Learning to spell: Research, theory, and practice across languages* (pp. 271-293). Mahwah, NJ: Lawrence Erlbaum Associates.

Felton, R. H. (1992). Early identification of children at risk for reading disabilities. *Topics in Early Childhood Special Education, 12*(2), 212-229.

Felton, R. H. & Brown, I. S. (1990). Phonological processes as predictors of specific reading skills in children at risk for reading failure. *Reading and Writing: An Interdisciplinary Journal, 2,* 39-59.

Fox, R., & Routh, D. K. (1975). Analyzing spoken language into words, syllables, and phonemes: A developmental study. *Journal of Psycholinguisitic Research, 4,* 331-342.

Fox, B., & Routh, D. K. (1980). Phonemic analysis and severe reading disability in children. *Journal of Psycholinguistic Research, 9*(2), 115-119.

Fox, B., & Routh, D. K. (1984). Phonemic analysis and synthesis as word attack skills: Revisited. *Journal of Educational Psychology, 76*(6), 1059-1064.

Frith, U. (1985). Beneath the surface of developmental dyslexia. In K. Patterson, J. Marshall, & M. Coltheart (Eds.), *Surface dyslexia: Neuropsychological and cognitive studies of phonological reading* (pp. 301-330). London: Lawrence Erlbaum Associates.

Gentry, J. R. (1982). An analysis of developmental spelling in GYNS AT WRK. *The Reading Teacher, 36*, 192-200.

German, D. (2000). *Test of word finding—second edition.* Austin, TX: Pro-Ed.

Gilbertson, M., & Bramlett, R. K. (1998). Phonological awareness screening to identify at-risk readers: Implications for practitioners. *Language, Speech, and Hearing Services in Schools, 29*, 109-116.

Goldman, R., & Fristoe, M. (2000). *Goldman-Fristoe test of articulation-2.* Circle Pines, MN: American Guidance Service.

Goswami, U., & Bryant, P. E. (1990). *Phonological skills and learning to read.* Hillsdale, NJ: Lawrence Erlbaum Associates.

Goswami, U., & Bryant, P. (1992). Rhyme, analogy, and children's reading. In P. B. Gough, L. Ehri, & R. Treiman (Eds.), *Reading acquisition* (pp.46-63). Hillsdale, NJ: Lawrence Erlbaum Associates.

Guthrie, J. T., Wigfield, A., Metsala, J. L., & Cox, K. E. (1999). Motivational and cognitive predictors of text comprehension and reading amount. *Scientific Studies of Reading, 3*(3), 231-256.

Hall, S. L., & Moats, L. C. (1999). *Straight talk about reading: How parents can make a difference during the early years.* Lincolnwood, IL: Contemporary Books.

Hodson, B. W. (1986). *Assessment of Phonological Processes-Revised.* San Antonio, TX: The Psychological Corporation.

Hodson, B. W. (1994). Helping individuals become intelligible, literate, and articulate: The role of phonology. *Topics in Language Disorders, 14*(2), 1-16.

Hodson, B. W. (2002). Assessing & enhancing phonological/metaphonological skills. Paper presented at the meeting of Illinois Speech-Language-Hearing Association. Chicago, IL.

Hoover, W. A., & Gough, P. B. (1990). The simple view of reading. *Reading and Writing: An Interdisciplinary Journal, 2,* 127-160.

International Dyslexia Association. (2002). *Frequently asked questions: What is dyslexia?* [on line]. Available: <http://www.interdys.org/servlet/compose?section_id=5> [2002, March 21].

Jenkins, R. & Bowen, L. (1994). Facilitating development of preliterate children's phonological abilities. *Topics in Language Disorder,14*(2), 26-39.

Justice, L. M., Invernizzi, M. A., & Meier, J. D. (2002). Designing and implementing an early literacy screening protocol: Suggestions for the speech-language pathologist. *Language, Speech, and Hearing Services in Schools, 33,* 84-101.

Katz, R. B. (1986). Phonological deficiencies in children with reading disability: Evidence from an object-naming task. *Cognition, 22,* 225-257.

Katz, R. B., Shankweiler, D., & Liberman, I. Y. (1981). Memory for item order and phonetic recoding in the beginning reader. *Journal of Experimental Child Psychology, 32,* 474-484.

Khan, L., & Lewis, N. (2002). *Khan-Lewis phonological analysis* (2nd Ed.). Circle Pines, MN: American Guidance Service.

Kitchen, B. (1984). *Animal alphabet.* New York: Dial.

Lapp, D., Flood, F., Lungren, L., & Geiss, R. (2000). *CLUES for phonemic awareness.* Billerica, MA: Curriculum Associates.

Lachance, S. (2002). *Sounds abound: Storybook activities.* East Moline, IL: LinguiSystems.

Larrivee, L. S., & Catts, H. W. (1999). Early reading achievement in children with expressive phonological disorders. *American Journal of Speech-Language Pathology, 8,* 118-128.

Lenchner, O., & Podhajski, B. (1998). *The sounds abound program: Teaching phonological awareness in the classroom.* East Moline IL: LinguiSystems.

Liberman, I. Y. (1983). A language-oriented view of reading and its disabilities. In H. R. Myklebust (Ed.), *Progress in learning disabilities* (Vol. V, pp. 81-101). New York: Grune and Stratton.

Liberman, I., Shankweiler, D., Fischer, F., & Carter, B. (1974). Explicit syllable and phoneme segmentation in the young child. *Journal of Experimental Child Psychology, 18,* 201-212.

Lie, A. (1991). Effects of a training program for stimulating skills in word analysis in first-grade children. *Reading Research Quarterly, 26*(3), 234-250.

Lindamood, C. H., & Lindamood, P. C. (1971). *Lindamood auditory conceptualization test.* San Antonio, TX: The Psychological Corporation.

Lindamood, P., & Lindamood, P. (1998). *The Lindamood phoneme sequencing program for reading, spelling, and speech (The LiPS program).* Austin, TX: PRO-ED, Inc.

Lombardino, L. J., Bedford, T., Fortier, C., Carter, J., & Brandi, J. (1997). Invented spelling: Developmental patterns in kindergarten children and guidelines for early literacy intervention. *Language, Speech, and Hearing Services in Schools, 28,* 333-343.

Lombardino, L. J., Riccio, C. A., Hynd, G. W., & Pinheiro, S. B. (1997). Linguistic deficits in children with reading disabilities. *American Journal of Speech-Language Pathology*, *6*(3), 71-78.

Lundberg, I., Frost, J., & Peterson, O. (1988). Effects of an extensive program for stimulating phonological awareness in preschool children. *Reading Research Quarterly, 23*(3), 263-284.

Lyon, G. R. (1996). The state of research. In S. C. Cramer and W. Ellis (Eds.), *Learning disabilities: Lifelong issues* (pp. 3-61). Baltimore, MD: Paul H. Brookes.

Lyon, G. R. (2001). Measuring success: Using assessments and accountability to raise student achievement. Committee on Education and the Workforce Hearings [online]. Available: <http://edworkforce.house.gov/hearings/107th/edr/account3801/lyon.htm > [2002, February 13].

MacDonald, G. W., & Cornwall, A. (1995). The relationship between phonological awareness and reading and spelling achievement eleven years later. *Journal of Learning Disabilities, 28*(8), 523-527.

Magnusson, E., & Naucler, K. (1990). Can preschool data predict language-disordered children's reading and spelling at school? *Folia Phoniatrica, 42*(6), 277-282.

Mann, M. (1999). *The Sixties TV Sound Tape* [audiotape]. New York: Mercury Records.

Mann, V. A., & Liberman, I. Y. (1984). Phonological awareness and verbal short-term memory. *Journal of Learning Disabilities, 17*(10), 592-599.

Martin, B., Jr. (1983). *Brown bear, brown bear, what do you see?* New York: Holt, Rinehart, and Winston.

Martin, B., Jr. (1989*). Chicka chicka boom boom.* New York: Simon and Shuster.

Menyuk, P., Chesnick, M., Liebergott, J. W., Korngold, B., D'Agostino, R., & Belanger, A. (1991). Predicting reading problems in at-risk children. *Journal of Speech and Hearing Research, 34*, 893-903.

Moats, L. C. (1995). *Spelling: Development, disability, and instruction.* Baltimore, MD: York Press.

Moats, L. C. (1998). Teaching decoding. *American Educator, 22*(1-2), 42-49, 95-96.

Morais, J., Bertelson, P., Cary, L., & Alegria, J. (1986). Literacy training and speech segmentation. *Cognition, 24*, 45-64.

Morais, J., Cary, L., Alegria, J., & Bertelson, P. (1979). Does awareness of speech as a sequence of phones arise spontaneously? *Cognition, 7*, 323-331.

More silly songs [compact disc]. (1998). Burbank, CA: Walt Disney Records.

Morris, D., & Perney, J. (1984). Developmental spelling as a predictor of first-grade reading achievement. *The Elementary School Journal, 84*(4), 441-457.

Mosel, Arlene. (1968). *Tikki Tikki Tembo.* New York: Holt, Rinehart, and Winston.

Muter, V., Hulme, C., & Snowling, M. (1997). *Phonological abilities test.* San Antonio: TX: The Psychological Corporation.

Nation, K., & Snowling, M. J. (1998). Semantic processing and the development of word-recognition skills: Evidence from children with reading comprehension difficulties. *Journal of Memory and Language, 39*, 85-101.

National Center for Learning Disabilities. (2002). About LD: LD basics. [Online] Available: <http://www.ncld.org/info/index.cfm> [2002, March 21].

Nelson, N. (1998). *Childhood language disorder in context: Infancy through adolescence.* Boston: Allyn & Bacon.

Newcomer, P., & Hammill, D. (1988). *Test of language development—2 primary.* Austin, TX: PRO-ED, Inc.

Owens, R. E., Jr. (1996). *Language development: An introduction.* Boston: Allyn and Bacon.

Perfetti, C. A. (1991). Representations and awareness in the acquisition of reading competence. In L. Rieben & C. A. Perfetti (Eds.), *Learning to read: Basic research and its implications* (pp. 33-44). Hillsdale, NJ: Lawrence Erlbaum Associates.

Raffi. (1976). *Singable songs for the very young* [compact disc]. Universal City, CA: MCA/Rounder.

Raffi. (1989). *Raffi in concert with the Rise and Shine Band* [compact disc]. Cambridge, MA: Rounder/MCA/Shoreline/Troubadour.

Rapala, M. M., & Brady, S. (1990). Reading ability and short-term memory: The role of phonological processing. *Reading and Writing*: *An Interdisciplinary Journal, 2,* 1-25.

Read, C. (1971). Pre-school children's knowledge of English phonology. *Harvard Educational Review, 41*(1), 1-34.

Read, C., & Ruyter, L. (1985). Reading and spelling skills in adults of low literacy. *Remedial and Special Education, 6*(6), 43-52.

Robertson, C., & Salter, W. (1995a). *The phonological awareness kit: Primary.* East Moline, IL: LinguiSystems.

Robertson, C., & Salter, W. (1995b). *The phonological awareness profile.* East Moline, IL: LinguiSystems.

Robertson, C., & Salter, W. (1997). *The phonological awareness test.* East Moline, IL: LinguiSystems.

Salisbury, K. (1997). *My nose is a hose!* New York: McClanahan Book Co.

Salisbury, K. (1997). *There's a bug in my mug!* New York: McClanahan Book Co.

Salisbury, K. (1998). *A bear ate my pear!* New York: McClanahan Book Co.

Salisbury, K. (1998). *There's a dragon in my wagon!* New York: McClanahan Book Co.

Scarborough, H. S. (1990). Very early language deficits in dyslexic children. *Child Development, 61,* 1728-1743.

Sesame Street. (1996). *Sesame Street: Sing the alphabet* [audiotape]. New York: Sony Wonder.

Shriberg, L. D., & Kent, R. D. (1995). *Clinical phonetics* (2nd Ed.). Boston: Allyn & Bacon.

Slepian, J., & Seidler, A. (1990). *The hungry thing returns.* New Jersey: Penguin.

Slepian, J., & Seidler, A. (2001). *The hungry thing.* Topeka, KN: Econo-Clad.

Smiley, S. S., Oakley, D. D., Worthen, D., Campione, J. C., & Brown, A. L. (1977). Recall of thematically relevant material by adolescent good and poor readers as a function of written versus oral presentation. *Journal of Educational Psychology, 69*(4), 381-387.

Smith, C. R. (1998). From gibberish–phonemic awareness: Effective decoding instruction. *Teaching Exceptional Children,* July/August, 20-25.

Snow, C. E., Burns, M. S., & Griffin, P. (Eds.). (1998). *Preventing reading difficulties in young children.* Washington, D.C: National Academy Press.

Snow, C. E., Scarborough, H. S., & Burns, M. S. (1999). What speech-language pathologists need to know about early reading. *Topics in Language Disorders, 20*(1), 48-58.

Snowling, M. J. (1981). Phonemic deficits in developmental dyslexia. *Psychological Research, 43*, 219-234.

Stanovich, K. E. (1986). Matthew effects in reading: Some consequences of individual differences in the acquisition of literacy. *Reading Research Quarterly, 21*(4), 360-406.

Stanovich, K. E., Cunningham, A. E., & Cramer, B. B. (1984). Assessing phonological awareness in kindergarten children: Issues of task comparability. *Journal of Experimental Child Psychology, 38*, 175-190.

Stoel-Gammon, C. (1987). Phonological skills of two-year-olds. *Language, Speech, and Hearing Services in Schools. 18*, 323-329.

Stoel-Gammon, C., & Dunn, C. (1985). *Normal and disordered phonology in children.* Austin, TX: PRO-ED, Inc.

Stone, B., & Brady, S. (1995). Evidence for phonological processing deficits in less-skilled readers. *Annals of Dyslexia, 45*, 51-78.

Swank, L. K. (1994). Phonological coding abilities: Identification of impairments related to phonologically based reading problems. *Topics in Language Disorders, 14*(2), 56-71.

Swank, L. K., & Catts, H. W. (1994). Phonological awareness and written word decoding. *Language, Speech, and Hearing Services in Schools, 25,* 9-14.

Teachworth, J. (2001). *Sounds abound: Multisensory phonological awareness.* East Moline, IL: LinguiSystems.

Templeton, S. (2002). Spelling logical, learnable, and critical. *ASHA Leader, 7*(3), 4-5, 12.

Torgesen, J. K. (1985). Memory processes in reading disabled children. *Journal of Learning Disabilities, 18*(6), 350-357.

Torgesen, J. K. (1995). *Phonological awareness: A critical factor in dyslexia.* Baltimore: Orton Dyslexia Society.

Torgesen, J. K. (1998). Catch them before they fall: Identification and assessment to prevent reading failure in young children. *American Educator*, spring/summer, 32-39.

Torgeson, J. K. (1999). Assessment and instruction for phonemic awareness and word recognition skills. In H. W. Catts & A. G. Kamhi (Eds.), *Language and Reading Disabilities* (pp. 128-153). Boston, MA: Allyn & Bacon.

Torgesen, J. K., & Bryant, B. (1994 a). *Phonological awareness training program.* Austin, TX: PRO-ED, Inc.

Torgesen, J. K., & Bryant, B. R. (1994 b). *Test of phonological awareness.* San Antonio: TX: The Psychological Corporation.

Torgesen, J. K., & Burgess, S. R. (1998). Consistency of reading-related phonological processes throughout early childhood: Evidence from longitudinal-correlational and instructional studies. In J. Metsala & L. Ehri (Eds.), *Word recognition in beginning literacy* (pp. 161-189). Hillsdale, NJ: Lawrence Erlbaum Associates.

Torgesen, J. K., Wagner, R. K., & Rashotte, C. A. (1994). Longitudinal studies of phonological processing and reading. *Journal of Learning Disabilities, 27*(5), 276-286.

Tunmer, W. E., Herriman, M. L., & Nesdale, A. R. (1988). Metalinguistic abilities and beginning reading. *Reading Research Quarterly, 23*(2), 134-158.

van Kleeck, A. (1998). Preliteracy domains and stages: Laying the foundations for beginning reading. *Journal of Children's Communication Development, 20*(1), 33-51.

Vellutino, F. R., Scanlon, D. M., & Spearing, D. (1995). Semantic and phonological coding in poor and normal readers. *Journal of Experimental Child Psychology, 59*, 76-123.

Wagner, R., Balthazor, M., Hurley, S., Morgan, S., Rashotte, C., Shaner, R., Simmons, K., & Stage, S. (1987). The nature of prereaders' phonological processing abilities. *Cognitive Development, 2*, 355-373.

Wagner, R. K., & Torgesen, J. K. (1987). The nature of phonological processing and its causal role in the acquisition of reading skills. *Psychological Bulletin, 101*(2), 192-212.

Wagner, R. K., Torgesen, J. K., & Rashotte, C. A. (1994). Development of reading-related phonological processing abilities: New evidence of bidirectional causality from a latent variable longitudinal study. *Developmental Psychology, 30*(1), 73-87.

Wagner, R. K., Torgesen, J. K., & Rashotte, C. (1999). *Comprehensive test of phonological processing.* Austin, TX: PRO-ED, Inc.

Warner, M. (1999). *Just for me! Phonological awareness.* East Moline, IL: LinguiSystems.

Webster, P. E., & Plante, A. S. (1992). Effects of phonological impairment on word, syllable, and phoneme segmentation and reading. *Language, Speech and Hearing Services in Schools, 23*, 176-182.

Wells, R. (1997). *Noisy Nora.* New York: Dial Books for Young Readers.

Wolf, M., Bally, H., & Morris, R. (1986). Automaticity, retrieval processes, and reading: A longitudinal study in average and impaired readers. *Child Development, 57*, 988-1000.

Wylie, R. E., & Durrell, D. D. (1970). Teaching vowels through phonograms. *Elementary English, 47,* 787-791.

Yopp, H. K. (1992). Developing phonemic awareness in young children. *The Reading Teacher, 45*(9), 696-703.

Ziefert, H. (1997). *Henny Penny.* New York: Viking.